*What readers have s*

## *Reports from Coastal Stations*

*A great read!*

*..getting there and back made very entertaining reading..*

*...very much enjoyed your geographical, historical and transport details!*

*... love the people bits, the encounters...*

*... incorporates travel, historic and scientific details in a seamless manner..*

*... quite an odyssey ...*

*... read it all inside 24 hours. A great read!*

*I now know an interesting fact about plaice...*

# REPORTS FROM COASTAL STATIONS

Journeys to the Weather Stations

Reported on the

BBC Shipping Forecast

## Geoff Saunders

# Reports from Coastal Stations

ISBN 978-0-9568532-0-2

First Published April 2011

By Suffix

Forge House, Ansell Road,

Dorking, Surrey RH4 1UN

Reprinted August 2011

For my Family and Friends

# Contents

# The Origins of an Odyssey

How long have I wanted to write this story? How many of us have awoken early or late to hear the soft tones of the BBC deliver the Shipping Forecast, warnings of gales later, good becoming moderate? And then, 'Weather Reports from Coastal Stations': observations of actual weather from around the fringes of our islands, names familiar yet remote. How many people go on to wonder about the coastal stations themselves, from which the weather reports emanate? Are these wild and weather-battered lighthouses or coast guard stations, once warmed against the winter gales by smoky coal fires but now deserted? Or do people still actually gather the data, read barometers and rain gauges before preparing their stylised reports for transmission? That was the genesis of my idea, to visit each of these far-flung coastal stations, find out what is there and then write my own report!

I daydreamed often of what it would be like, of how to accomplish a journey to each of these locations, of whether it should be in winter or summer, or in my madder moments, both! Perhaps I could visit them all on a single journey around the extremities of the islands? Clockwise, starting with Tiree, would be the direction in which they are read, so perhaps that was the way to go. That would certainly be fun, and the journey around the extremes would be a real challenge too. But then reality struck home. If I waited until I had the time to do this, it would never happen. Little did I realise just how difficult it would be, nor how long it would take, to visit them all irrespective of the season. Nor did I realise how much fun I would have making journeys to each as and when I had the time.

Somehow there were always other things that came first. Not insignificant things either. I have been very lucky in my travels, both for work and for pleasure. Indeed, sometimes when faced with the question on an immigration form, 'Business or Pleasure?' I have been hard pressed to decide. There is never an option that says "It's a pleasure doing business here!" My family have always given me great support for those travels, sometimes joining me, and sometimes just wishing me well as I set sail for some distant horizon. Their support would be needed again if I was to undertake these rather curious journeys nearer to home.

I was born and brought up in Dublin, a sea port since well before the Vikings arrived to build the first recorded harbour. From my classroom, I could see Dublin's docks and the lights of the harbour entrance. So I well remember the changing weather, and of course we always listened out for the forecast for sea area 'Irish Sea'. As the winter gales rattled the tiles on our house, my mother would look up and softly say her prayer – "Heaven help the sailors on a night like this!"

Although we like to make light of the weather forecasts' accuracy, (and who will ever forget Michael Fish?), we have all had cause to be grateful for those forecasts, at home or away on a distant ocean. It may sound obvious, but forecasts depend on observations. At that same school I learned something of the making of those observations, then later I had opportunities to observe, and to teach others, at home and abroad. We tend to think nowadays that weather satellites watch our weather, and do all the necessary measurements required. But there is no substitute for observations on the ground, or out in the ocean, at sea level. Satellite instruments need calibration, confirmation that they really do provide useful information. Remote sensing depends on assumptions, and these constantly need refinement. For instance, satellite measurements of ozone in the atmosphere detected the 'ozone hole' over Antarctica long before it was recognised. In the absence of corroborating ground-based evidence, the satellite observations were dismissed as anomalous, aberrations of the instruments due perhaps to the special nature of the Antarctic atmosphere. It was not until scientists at the British Antarctic Survey's Faraday Base started to take similar measurements that the satellite readings were accepted as true readings, and the world woke up to the damage caused to the atmosphere by CFC's. Like boots on the ground for the army, in-situ observations are indispensable for reliable forecasting.

The coastal stations featured in the BBC Shipping Forecast are just a selection of the dozens of places where weather is recorded for the Met Office, but they represent something of the extremes of our islands. They sit on the very edges of our shores, spread out to give as complete a picture of the actual weather as possible, and allow comparison with previous forecasts. So any plan to visit them is in itself a journey of extremes. In fact, I had come close to visiting the general vicinity of just about all the coastal station locations over the years. These extremes have always had their own fascination for me. The small communities that perch on the edges of our islands have an allure that only rarely makes its way into the travel pages of the papers. Yet they have much to offer but, of course, lack the sunshine of the usual exotic destinations, and their often dramatic weather can be daunting. Perhaps my interest in small islands and remote places started when I was young. My first 'overseas' holiday from Dublin began with the short flight aboard an Aer Lingus Dakota travelling to the Isle of Man, where we landed at Ronaldsway Airport, the most central of the reporting stations!

Also in my youth, I remember reading of weather ships, deployed far out in the Atlantic, gathering information beyond our shores, and assisting transatlantic aircraft with navigation. What a lonely posting that must have been. These have long been replaced by automatic buoys, but the intention is the same, corroborating and re-calibrating observations so that we have as reliable a picture of the actual weather as possible. A network of buoys, called Marine Automatic Weather Stations (MAWS), now surrounds our coasts. They are deployed, some far out in the Atlantic, by the weather services of many European nations, who share the information amongst themselves and also with the wider scientific community. A huge amount of this weather data, for Europe and for the wider world, is readily and easily available from the US National Oceanic and Atmospheric Administration's web site[1].

Sharing this data around the world is essential because the world's oceans and atmosphere together form a giant system for distributing heat and moisture around the globe. Weather knows no national boundaries. We regularly hear of El Niño and its impact on weather, and climate, far away from its location in the central Pacific. Not surprisingly, therefore, the central Pacific area is well provided with observation buoys, and criss-crossed by commercial ships making observations too. But look a little further south on a globe and you quickly realise that the South Pacific Ocean is a vast area, with a sprinkling of islands, and very little traffic. Weather observations from here are few and far between, so the world weather community jumps at the chance to have direct readings from these locations whenever possible.

Some of my more exciting travels have taken me into this region aboard the square-rigged sailing ship *Soren Larsen*[2] which for a number of years has been making an annual voyage through the remote Polynesian islands from a base in Auckland. Paying 'voyage crew' join as temporary sailors for a few weeks or months at a time, as the ship uses the spectacular islands as stepping stones to cross the vast ocean. Sailing between these stepping stones, Easter Island and Pitcairn for example, two of the most remote communities on earth, you can be fairly confident that actual weather observations will be rare indeed. As a matter of course, during any of these voyages, we record simple weather observations every hour, along with a summary of the ship's state. But when out at sea, and far from land, every six hours the ship's officers, with the help of interested sailors like myself, make a more detailed and formal set of observations of the weather, and of the sea itself. These are then coded up on International Maritime Organisation log sheets as a series of numbers, and transmitted via a satellite link to the appropriate weather bureau. I don't suppose we changed the course of history with our readings, but we did derive a certain satisfaction from knowing our work contributed to the faxed forecasts we subsequently received from the same weather bureau. We were always grateful for these forecasts, even though they were often rather vague, of necessity in such a vast ocean. But on more than one occasion, though thankfully not while I was aboard, the ship's company had particular cause to be very grateful, when advance warning of severe storms enabled them to make preparations and to take avoiding action.

How different it would have been for Captain Robert Fitzroy on the *Beagle*. Many times he must have wished he had had some notice of impending storms, or calms. Perhaps during the voyage he did his own thinking about the weather, and maybe even formulated his thoughts 'On the Origin of Weather Systems' while his companion, Charles Darwin, was puzzling on other Origins. Aboard the sailing ship *Soren Larsen* I was lucky enough to visit Darwin's famous stamping ground, the Galapagos Islands. Of course much has changed since his visit. Chiefly these changes are the result of settlers from the mainland, desperate to escape poverty, colonizing a land with no indigenous human habitation. The effects are all too clear: introduced species run amok, a small scale and vivid illustration of the impact humans make on the planet.

Approaching the islands, we recorded the sea surface temperature along with the other weather parameters, looking for, and finding, the famous Humboldt Current which surfaces in this region. It brings chilly water from the deep ocean, and along with it, nutrients that feed the chain of life, so evident in the extraordinary diversity of sea life in these regions. Fitzroy would have noticed too that the chilly water influences the local weather, shrouding the islands frequently in mist, and making them hard to find at times, hence their designation by the whalers as the Enchanted Islands.

Certainly my interest in our own weather was augmented by these travels, but in any case the Shipping Forecast and its Reports from Coastal Stations was always there when I returned. Those magic glimpses of diverse locations around the shores of our own islands continued to beckon. And now I had personal experience of what was involved in collecting weather data in the way our weather stations do for us. If I could see how weather observations were made in remote oceans, surely it should be a lot easier to see the process nearer to home?

Of course, it would be possible to fulfil this dream by simply throwing money at it. I could fly to the nearest airport, and take a taxi or hire car for a quick spin. Then, after the required photo opportunity, I could rush off to the next one on the list. A glance at the map shows that all the coastal stations are remarkably, though not accidentally, near an airport. Somehow this didn't seem a satisfactory way to approach the task though. Similarly, to drive from home on a 'round the island' route would be interesting, and a considerable challenge in its own right, but somehow that too would seem to be cheating. I wanted a challenge that I thought really worthy of the objective. If I could accomplish the visits by public transport, without flying, that would be a challenge indeed! Some of the offshore stations would need sea-borne transport for sure, and that might only be possible with a boat, hired, borrowed or shared, but the details would emerge later. For now though, I had the scope of my self-imposed challenge, and amused my family and friends discussing my half-formed plans to accomplish it. I also listened to their suggestions as to how to reach the various stations, and wondered how many of them I could get to accompany me.

As part of my planning and my travels to find the various coastal stations, I learned many things. I suppose I was vaguely aware of the place of Robert Fitzroy (chiefly known, if at all, as the Captain of the *Beagle*) in the history of the Met Office. Prompted by the loss of the passenger vessel *Royal Charter* and 459 of its passengers and crew off the coast of North Wales in a violent storm in 1859, the

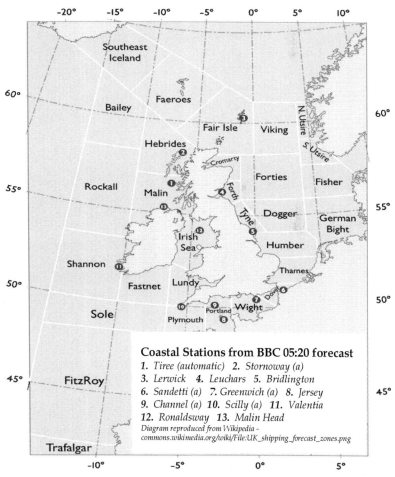

Coastal Stations from BBC 05:20 forecast
1. *Tiree (automatic)* 2. *Stornoway (a)*
3. *Lerwick* 4. *Leuchars* 5. *Bridlington*
6. *Sandetti (a)* 7. *Greenwich (a)* 8. *Jersey*
9. *Channel (a)* 10. *Scilly (a)* 11. *Valentia*
12. *Ronaldsway* 13. *Malin Head*
Diagram reproduced from Wikipedia -
commons.wikimedia.org/wiki/File:UK_shipping_forecast_zones.png

British Government appointed Fitzroy to try to develop a national gale warning service. But only gradually did it become clear to me just what he did, and what he used. By 1860 Fitzroy had established a network of thirteen coastal stations[3] from which weather observations were made and visual gale warnings displayed, day and night, for ships at sea. Many sailors had reason to be grateful for the advanced warning of heavy weather while in proximity to land. Out at sea, gales were less dangerous to shipping because they had space to manoeuvre, sea room, and could run before heavy weather, or simply sit it out. Near land, there was no such luxury. The nightmare of every captain was being caught in a storm on a 'lee shore', that is with the wind blowing the ship towards the shore, and nowhere to shelter. Unlike modern yachts, or ancient Polynesian sailing canoes, square rigged ships could make very little progress to windward, none into a storm. Early warning of an impending gale gave the captain the chance to head back out to sea, to gain 'sea room' to ride out the storm safely, if uncomfortably for the passengers and crew.

Fitzroy himself coined the phrase 'weather forecast', but his limited means prevented more than a 24-hour look ahead with any accuracy at all. At first I wondered as to how he managed to make observations of weather which would still be current by the time they reached his office. But gradually I realised that his work began at about the same time the telegraph was invented and began to be used for important message transmission. This invention allowed him to receive the observations, make his calculations and return 'forecast' weather reports to the coastal stations. Amusingly, the Admiralty seemed more concerned with the cost of the telegrams[4] than with the value of the forecasts.

Since 'wireless telegraphy' had not yet been invented, reception of the forecast weather depended on vessels sighting a coastal station and its weather signals. Fitzroy invented a series of signals[5] that would be readily visible, day and night, as warnings of impending bad weather. I was surprised to find that these signals were still in use, hoisted at irregular intervals, on the Signal Station at Jersey. From September 1860 the weather forecasts developed by Fitzroy were published in the newspapers and eventually broadcast from coastal radio stations and ultimately by the BBC, where it gradually changed into the form we now know. Sadly it seems his attempts to further extend the forecasts led him to draw conclusions which could not be supported. He argued with many others trying to produce forecasts in France and America, then in circumstances that are unclear, cut his own throat and died. A terrible end to a very distinguished career.

Mostly on land we tend to listen out for the weather forecast, worrying if our plans for the weekend will have to change, or if we should take an umbrella to the office. But its origin is as a safety measure for shipping, only later being used by the general public, and now feeding something of a national obsession. Vast amounts of money are spent on forecasting for commercial purposes too. The obvious beneficiaries are the marine and aviation industries in their various guises.

The general nature of the Shipping Forecast is described in a Met Office document, available on the web.[6] As read out on Radio 4, it gives a summary of gale warnings in force, a general synopsis and area forecasts for specified sea areas around the UK. Some broadcasts include the latest available reports of actual weather, wind direction and force, visibility, sea-level atmospheric pressure and its recent movement, for a number of weather stations, referred to as 'Coastal Stations,' around the UK. These were my quarry!

But even these stations are not a simple quarry. At one time, not so long ago, these reports were read out after each Shipping Forecast on BBC Radio 4. Now they are only issued twice daily, at 00:48 and 05:20, and the stations reported in the two bulletins differ. To add to the confusion, for quite some time the reports themselves were not carried on the internet 'Listen Again' versions of the Shipping Forecast. However, recognising that change is really the only constant, I kept checking the BBC website, and eventually, in early 2010, my checks were rewarded with the ability to 'listen again' up to a week later. After the 00:48 bulletin on Radio 4, a much longer list of weather stations is used than after the 05:20 bulletin. I chose the shorter list as my target, but I may be persuaded to add the extra stations later as a sort of weather encore. Since each is now available on the BBC website, the really keen can catch both, without staying up very late, nor getting up very early.

Since the inception of the Shipping Forecast, there has been an evolution in both the shipping areas and the stations reporting actual weather. Much to the consternation of land-based purists, shipping areas have been divided, extended, modified and even renamed at different times ever since their inception. Strangely, there were even many objections to the renaming in 2002 of the 'Finisterre' area as 'Fitzroy', in honour of the founder of the Met Office. I'm not aware of any such outcry over the choice of coastal stations, though. A glance at the Met Office records online gives something of this history. I remember from some distant point in my past hearing of a 'Royal Sovereign' station. This was a lightship off the Eastbourne coast, which was replaced by a platform in 1971, and automated in 1994. It probably still sends weather reports to the Met Office, but its reports are no longer used in the BBC bulletins.

More worryingly for me, during the time it took for me to undertake my self-imposed task, another change was made. Fife Ness Coastal Station, a regular for many years, was replaced in the BBC list by Leuchars, an RAF air station nearby. Since their inception, the location of the observation points at the coastal stations have altered many times in response to technology, and the needs of users of the weather services. So my final list is of the ones currently in use, but where appropriate, I have referenced earlier stations that served a similar area.

The Fact Sheet on the Met Office web site, mentioned earlier, gives a very full definition of all the terms used in the Weather Reports from Coastal Stations. So if you have ever wondered what 'Mainly good' or 'Rising slowly' means, you can get a complete description of these and other terms and the way they are used, at the click of a mouse. The Met Office web site itself[7] is the key to a veritable wonderland of weather data, much readily accessible, some offered for sale to commercial interests, or detailed information offered to yachtsmen on a premium rate number. More rapidly than the list of coastal stations, the web site undergoes regular changes, usually, but not always, making more information available. After regularly checking the weather reported from one of the lightships (Greenwich) I was surprised to find it suddenly became accessible only with a secure password. However, an email to the appropriate authorities quickly restored my previous unhindered access. The ways of the web are wondrous indeed!

But I needed something to kick start my quest, or it would remain a dream. Then the chance came to make that start, and with one of the most difficult to reach stations, the Channel Light Vessel. Almost before I realised it, my weather Odyssey had begun, and my dilemma about the order in which to make the visits was resolved. I would take a pragmatic approach and visit each as the opportunity arose, or when I could make the opportunity arise!

---

[1] See www.noaa.gov for a wealth of weather and ocean information.

[2] See www.sorenlarsen.co.nz

[3] Aberdeen, Berwick, Hull, Yarmouth, Dover, Portsmouth, Plymouth, Penzance, Cork, Galway, Portrush, Greenock; See Report of Meteorological Department, 16th June 1860, note from Robert Fitzroy.

[4] Report of the Meteorological Department, letter to Fitzroy from the Admiralty, 23rd August 1860.

[5] See Appendix 1 for examples of Fitzroy's signals, and Met Office Library and Archive Fact Sheet no 8 for a fuller description of these signals.

[6] Met Office, library and archive, Fact Sheet Number 8 – The Shipping Forecast.

[7] www.metoffice.gov.uk.

# Channel Light Vessel (Automatic)

49° 54′ N        2° 53′ W

South southwest 4, 25 miles, Fair, 1001, Falling

May 2003

By chance, the opportunity came to make this station the badly needed push required to start my quest. It came about unexpectedly, and so I counted myself very lucky indeed to have this, one of the most difficult stations to visit, as the starting line. I probably would never have thought of starting my quest in this way, but then I had thought so much about it, and done nothing concrete, that I would have jumped at any chance to get started. And I didn't have to work out how to get there, the choice of transport was already made for me. Given that choice of transport, I had no real say as to the season. In any case, visiting the Channel Lightship in anything but fine weather would be foolhardy to say the least.

Simon had married a school friend, made on the first day at grammar school, of my lady love, Ginny. When he retired early, from a life spent in the board rooms of some of the world's major companies, be bought a motor cruising boat, the aptly named *Fearless II*. Since he and his wife had a holiday cottage in Brixham, it was the obvious place to moor the boat, in the well appointed marina. Being semi-retired myself, or at least aspiring to be so, I was one of his very few possible boating partners, so I willingly teamed up. He knew of my interest in boats, and something of my experiences sailing in the Pacific and elsewhere. And we had sailed together as guests aboard the Brixham trawler *Leader* along the south Devon and Cornwall coasts some years previously. Though we were, and remain, politically and ideologically poles apart, I liked to think that he valued my experience, if not my knowledge of sailing and the sea. For my part, I was pleased to be trusted as a boating companion, and relished the chance to spend a little more time messing about in boats.

Motor cruising may not be my favourite mode of sea travel, and indeed some of my sailing buddies were sceptical, not to say sniffy, about my new boating endeavours. But there is a saying that "A day spent at sea, on the poorest vessel, beats the best day working!" We spent quite a few weekends happily messing about in Brixham and gradually we got to know the boat, its capabilities and its limitations. Armed with this new knowledge and experience, we began to explore a little further along the coast from Brixham, enjoying the delights of Devonport and Salcombe. Indeed it was not long before we began to set our sights on travels further around the west of England, and examined eagerly the charts for Cornwall, the Isles of Scilly, the Channel Islands and beyond.

However, weather and other commitments limited the scope for putting most of these plans into effect. The sea-keeping qualities of a motor cruiser scarcely fit it for travel in anything but the calmest weather. We were highly dependent on the local shipping forecast, and for any journey offshore we would be completely dependent on a settled sea state in the Channel. *Fearless II* depended for its speed on being able to plane like a speed boat, and so was uncomfortable and even dangerous in even relatively small waves. Reducing speed, so the boat could no longer plane, made it wallow and roll while the large engines drank fuel very inefficiently.

But we did make progress with navigation and general seamanship, aided I like to think by my many months of sailing square-rigged ships across distant oceans. Enthused by our progress, we began to plan a Channel Island trip and we discussed our first crossing, to Guernsey, in the warmth and smog of a then smoke-filled Surrey pub. Something quickly caught my eye. An obvious way-point was none other than the Channel Light Vessel. My interest was doubled! Until then, I had only vague notions of how or when I might start my quest, and the dream had seemed destined to remain just that. But there it was, and the chart clearly indicated the navigational parameters of the light. In nautical language; Fl 15s 12m 15M. Meaning, in everyday terms, that the light is 12 metres above the sea, visible normally from 15 (nautical) miles away and flashes every 15 seconds.

A Channel crossing may seem a fairly simple venture, and with modern navigational aids, chiefly GPS, scarcely a major challenge. But taking a small boat well out of sight of land demands more than a modicum of care, a point insisted upon by our respective ladies. So a mid-Channel check point to verify our course, and instrument reading, would be most welcome. In fact, the Channel Light Vessel serves as the marker for the start of one of the marine traffic separation zones, Europe bound traffic keeping to the south while vessels outbound from Europe keep north. So it would also serve as a refuge from the busy traffic.

We planned the trip carefully. Venturing offshore in a motor cruiser is not to be undertaken lightly. While the boat is reasonably safe at sea, it cannot travel at any speed into a strong wind, or into a steep swell. We would be dependent on speed to make the journey, to take advantage of the limited weather windows available. From my own experience, I knew that channel crossings were challenging. The previous year I had sailed across in a small boat further east, from Chichester Harbour to Cherbourg. Avoiding the shipping in a sailing boat is even more of a challenge, since you travel so slowly in relation to modern ships. Landlubbers may quote 'steam gives way to sail' but I assure you that no reasonable sailing skipper would ever expect to cross shipping lanes relying on that ancient dictum. At least in a motor cruiser we would have some speed, closer to that of the ships, and easy manoeuvrability. To undertake the passage safely, you must be aware of the seas, the large ships, and the wind shifts to be expected as well as the rules of the sea. Weather conditions are vitally important.

A major milestone in our ability to use the boat for crossing the Channel would be to take it out of sight of land. So as a training exercise, we decided to go about half way, and return. This would limit our need for a weather window longer than a few hours, and would give us a feel for the boat away from land, in the bigger swells that are found far out in the Channel. We planned to take it to the edge of the traffic separation zone, itself marked by a navigation buoy, and then back. It turned out to be a worthwhile exercise.

The forecast suggested a short weather window, with rather rougher seas than we would normally want to make a crossing. But we decided to grab the opportunity. The journey out was trying, heading into a big swell. On each crest, we learned to swerve to avoid a noisy crunch if the bow landed too heavily. Crockery rattled loudly below, while anything not secured skidded across the deck, though nothing broke. We reached the navigation light at the edge of the separation zone in the early evening. In theory, we might have expected to catch a glimpse of the Channel Light Vessel signal, but as often happens, there was a low mist reducing visibility considerably, perhaps to 5 miles or so. We rested briefly in an uncomfortable swell before turning for home. On the return journey, with the swell behind us, the boat was considerably more comfortable, but standing in the open for so long was very cold. Back in the marina we listed our 'lessons learned', and developed revised plans for the full crossing.

A week or so later, the omens came together again. I was working in London, and instead of getting my train home to Dorking after work, I boarded a Great Western train at Paddington for Paignton. I settled into to a routine that would become something of the norm for many a future coastal station journey. Equipped with sandwiches and reading matter, the suburbs and then the countryside slipped by. It was dark by the time I arrived at Paignton station, but Simon was there to meet me and we sped through quiet streets to Brixham, a few preparatory pints as we rehearsed the plans and then an early night.

In the morning, we did the, by now customary, preparations but then unusually checked out with the Marina office. They advised that we call the coastguard as we left the harbour, to report our destination, expected passage time and numbers aboard. Though not legally required, it certainly makes sense for any small boat attempting a channel crossing to check out on departure, and then check in on arrival at the other side. The latter is very important, though failure to do so would not necessarily trigger any kind of search.

We were better prepared for our journey than we had been for the earlier trial, and, with tips and notes aplenty from our many planning sessions, we set off on a bright sunny May morning. This time we had no unfriendly swell to dodge. Instead a gentle tail wind pushed us easily along with a softly rolling swell from behind. The coastline faded into a warm mist, and was quickly lost from sight. We were well into the open waters of the Channel, making great progress at nearly full speed, 30 knots. At this rate we would arrive in about 5 hours.

Soon we were sighting, and then dodging, the ships in the westbound separation lane. Crossing a separation lane is a bit like crossing a motorway. You don't expect the traffic to avoid you; you must avoid it! However, on one occasion, a speeding ship did visibly alter course to pass behind us. Whether this was because of his intended course, perhaps a little to the north towards Ireland, or to be nice to us, we could not divine.  But it was a welcome manoeuvre, nonetheless.  It's amazing just how quickly ships appear on the horizon, enlarge, and bear down on a small boat. The obvious choice is to pass behind any large ship, but sometimes they appear in groups, and require careful calculation to keep a comfortable distance away.

While we steered a careful course between the westbound ships, I kept a sharp eye out for the distinctive light that would confirm our course.  Then, low down on the horizon, we glimpsed a flash.  This must have been close to the limit of visibility, for it was some time before the flash seemed to lift above the horizon, and before we saw the unmistakable silhouette of a light ship emerge from the horizon.  But the timing matched, 15 seconds between flashes, and as we came nearer we saw that its hull was painted red, with the word CHANNEL along its side!

The vessel is of course now unmanned, but at one time would have had a crew of three, relieved by boat every six weeks or so.  A helicopter deck shows its now normal mode of relief and service, though it would be fuelled from a tender at infrequent intervals.

So here we were at the westward point on the 'central reservation' of the traffic separation scheme.  It was an eerie feeling to be there, amongst the circling gannets, and to imagine what automatic weather report it was generating at that moment.  I felt rather privileged, to be one of very few people who actually get to see this icon of the weather bulletins.  On such a clear day, with visibility 'more than 25 miles', it all looked benign.  Sure there was the swell, perhaps 2 metres or more, on which the vessel gently rose and fell. But there was a gale forecast for the next 24 hours, a gale that would keep us in Guernsey for a few days.  It would look rather different then.  And I would have no way to witness this other extreme.

We posed for photos on the rear deck of our trusted *Fearless II*, not venturing too close to the lightship itself. It's a bit like resting on the central reservation of a motorway. To the north, ships headed

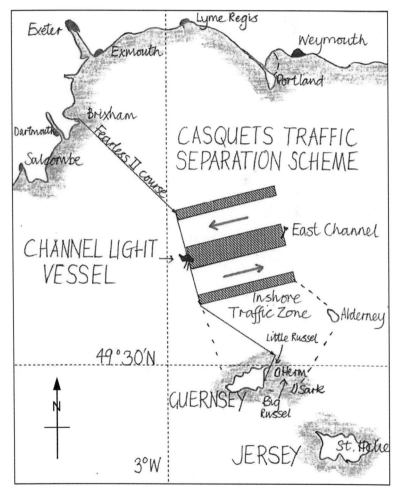

west, bound for who knows where. To the south, laden tankers and container vessels ploughed their way to Europe's great ports, oblivious of our little boat and our halt to catch our breath, and my secret quest!

Then it was off to complete our Channel crossing, while I felt quietly satisfied that I had perhaps the most difficult coastal station under my belt, a wonderful way to start the collection. But our adventures were far from over. A short time after leaving the southern, eastbound carriageway, we saw a similar boat to our own approaching from the southeast. It appeared to be heading straight for us, at full speed. We altered course to starboard, aiming to give it a wide berth, but as we turned we could see no one on the bridge of the other boat, no one anywhere in fact. Clearly the skipper had set the auto pilot for a suitable waypoint and disappeared below. Keeping a good lookout is the first duty of a mariner. And aren't we glad we did!

The approach to St. Peter Port on Guernsey is through quite a dangerous, though well marked navigation channel. Huge tides rush up and down the Little Russell Channel between Guernsey and Herm, requiring close attention to details during the approach. However, on arrival there is a large and well protected harbour, with a marina close to the town protected by a 'sill'. This limits the rise and fall of the tides, but also limits the hours when you can arrive and leave. Our arrival time was ideal, and we tied up at our allotted berth before celebrating with a large mug of tea.

I was intrigued to be in Guernsey again. My only previous visit had been as a young teenager, taking part in my first scout camp abroad. The journey from Dublin seemed endless, first the overnight mail boat across the Irish Sea, then a succession of trains, some steam-hauled, through Wales and England to Weymouth and another overnight boat to St. Peter Port. We must have been exhausted by the time we set up camp at a site near St. Sampson. I can time the journey as coincident with the Profumo affair which was unfolding during the journey, June 1963. Being young teenage boys, the not quite lurid details that were filling the papers at the time held us rapt. And away from our parents, we felt free to discuss them in a way we would never have done at home.

But the real wonder of the trip was yet to come. The holiday was enjoyable, but unremarkable until a group of girls about our own ages visited the camp. We chatted and played at nothing in particular, but one girl I though exceptionally lovely. When it was clear the thoughts were reciprocated, I imagined I had arrived in heaven. The remaining few days of our visit were spent in anticipation of the end of her school day, and of early evening walks, totally innocent. If I remember well she was fifteen, and about to leave school. Her ambition was to get a job in Woolworths, where her big sister worked. My own ambitions were rather different. We had a Saturday afternoon together before I was to leave, and we spent it with others of the group at the aptly named Ladies Bay. Warm hair, soft lips and innocent cuddles seemed the height of wonder, and we swore undying love, which lasted the exchange of about three letters.

Our arrival aboard *Fearless II* coincided with Liberation Day celebrations. After the success of the Normandy landings, the Allies moved on through France and the Low Countries, not quite forgetting about the Channel Islands. Understandably the generals were unwilling to expend military resources on a militarily useless objective, retaking the heavily fortified but completely isolated islands. Undefended, they had been abandoned by the British army after the fall of France, but their Nazi occupiers were incapable of making a similar judgement. Many more months of hardship and hunger awaited the islanders, the garrison and the considerable contingent of slave labourers toiling uselessly through the winter. While all of Western Europe celebrates 8th May as Liberation Day, in the Channel Islands it has to wait until 9th May[1], the day British troops again took control of the islands. As the only part of Britain to be occupied during the war, some grievance is felt and expressed about this delayed liberation. But no such concerns seemed to cloud the celebrations and fireworks we witnessed from our quayside vantage point that evening.

As forecast, the weather deteriorated after our arrival. Any thoughts of a visit to nearby Jersey and its own weather station, which appeared on Fitzroy's original list, flew away with the gale. Later and for many years Guernsey, not Jersey, was the representative weather station for the Islands, and it still has a weather station at its own airport. Just when and why these changes took place, I cannot say, but they probably coincided with available technology at each site. Instead of leaving as planned, we took a bus around the island, enjoying the windblown and wave spattered rocky coast with a feeling of relief, and gratitude for an accurate forecast. I looked for something of what I thought I remembered of Ladies Bay, but saw little to correspond with my teenage memory.

A few days stuck in any port can be a trial, but with the holiday closures and the bad weather we quickly ran out of diversionary activities. Guernsey has few attractions that would lead me to set up home there. A steady stream of off-islanders arrive for the tax breaks, but for the most part they seem to have abandoned culture along with the Inland Revenue. For company they have rich (but not very rich) neighbours whose common interest is money and property. I was keen to be away.

Fortunately, there was a forecast break in the weather, so we made preparations for an early morning departure. Tide tables told us we would have to leave the safety and comfort of the protected marina on the previous evening's high tide. We would spend a night tied up to a buoy in the main harbour, and then leave before the tide turned and raced back up the Little Russell Channel again.

As though preparing for a release from confinement, we prepared *Fearless II* for the voyage home. Everything that could fall or rattle was tied down, charts were laid out and fuel topped up. Again we were thankful for an accurate forecast as the sky cleared in the morning and we sped easily back towards the Channel Light Vessel, Brixham and home.

I was delighted with the outing. My quest had begun, perhaps the most difficult station had been visited, and I could plan more exciting trips with renewed enthusiasm. I even imagined I could complete the Odyssey within a year or so.

---

[1] www.guernseyliberationday.com/

# Sandettie (Automatic) – First Attempt

51° 7′ N          1° 48′ E

North northeast 6, 25 miles, Fair, 1008, Steady

March 2005

Having made the start with my quest, it was then quite a little while before I got the chance to visit a second coastal station on my list. Being an aspiring semi-retiree has its challenges. One is fighting off the offers of work, while another is finding enough time to do all the things you want to do, things like visiting coastal stations and then writing the reports from the visits. It's an amazing fact that the hypothetical list of things I would like to do just gets longer. Not that I'm lazy, it's just that I keep adding to the list faster than I can knock things off it. It seems that each thing I do prompts ideas to do several more. What I needed was a plan! After all, as an aspiring semi-retired project manager, what could be more natural than planning? Trouble is that takes time too. So I put together a spreadsheet, did some more general research and mapped out a possible way to accomplish all the visits in a couple of years. Optimist!

Just why I decided to try to make the Sandettie Light Vessel the second coastal station on my plan is no longer clear to me. Perhaps having started with a really hard one, the Channel Light, I thought I should get the hard ones out of the way at the start. If I couldn't get to the hard ones the quest would have no future. Also, Sandettie is something of a loner, and travel to it could not be combined with any other station. I should have realised that the attempt to reach it would not be simple. The only coastal station east of Greenwich, Sandettie Light Vessel is located at the southern end of the Sandettie sand bank, slap in the middle of the Dover Straits, one of the busiest shipping lanes in the world. But in theory, with the ferries criss-crossing the Strait, surely one should pass within sighting distance of the Light?

My chart of the Dover Strait was helpful. If you draw a straight line from Dover to Sandettie and continue on that line you arrive at Ostende. Now ferries rarely travel in straight lines across the shipping lanes. International 'rules for the avoidance of collisions at sea' oblige ships crossing such busy shipping lanes to do so at right angles. But it looked like the best chance. The only trouble is that there is no longer a ferry service between Dover and Ostende!

In my mind, that seemed to be one of the fixed reference points of continental travel, probably because my first ever crossing to the Continent, in my teens, was by that route. But I should know by now how rapidly things change. In consolation, looking for alternatives these days just requires a few key strokes for a Google search. This showed various ferries, but none on that route.

The most likely alternative I could find was a service between Dover and Dunkirk, operated by Norfolk Line. Their web site was helpful, but strangely they offered no passenger fares. A little further delving revealed that they were happy to carry bicycle passengers, but not foot passengers. I surmised this would be because of the need to provide some form of transport between the dock gates and the ship. A bicyclist has his own transport! If a bicycle was required, so be it.

Now the straight line joining Dover and Dunkirk passes a good deal south of Sandettie, but I reckoned that it may be possible to see the light from the ship, particularly if the right angle crossing of the separation zones took the ship north. It was worth a gamble at least. If it failed, all I would lose would be the modest fares and the day, while for compensation I would have a shopping trip to a French hypermarket and the possibility of a decent lunch to console myself.

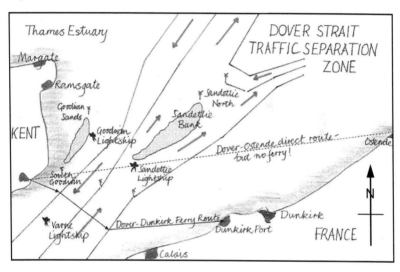

My day to travel arrived, and very early I was clambering up the twenty-nine steps to our local station, with my bike tucked perilously under my arm. Wonder of wonders, the train was on time, and the connection at Redhill was on time. The crunch would be at Tonbridge, but after another struggle with steps, and another on-time train, I was soon ensconced in comfort for the last hour of the rail journey. At Dover, I set out on my bike into the traffic, increasingly dominated by colossal trucks heading to or from the port.

Check-in was amusing.  Cycling up to the barrier, the attendant confessed that they did not get many bicycles travelling, just a few in the summer months.  I was able to join the head of the traffic queue, and with smiles and good wishes from the attendant soon embarked, locking my bike to a stanchion.  It quickly became clear that this was a freight service that allowed cars (and bikes), but its real purpose was the trucks and their drivers, for whom every effort was directed.  Despite some rather halfhearted signs, smoking seemed universal.  Hearty cooked breakfasts overflowing from large plates were the order of the day.  I can imagine I looked decidedly out of place, with my bowl of muesli and my fluorescent yellow cycling jacket.

For the first, but definitely not the last, time on this odyssey I decided to see if I could get some semi-official support.  So I approached the purser and made a polite request to visit the bridge.  After I had explained something of my wishes, my request was met with some enthusiasm and just a little amusement.  Once the ship had cleared the breakwater, the purser explained that I would be called over the public-address system and escorted to the bridge.  And so it was.  The bridge crew, which I was pleased to see included a female officer, were very happy to tell me about the running of the ship, the course, the controls and everything they could think of.  Despite a high level of automation, the bridge is a very busy place, and everyone there had important work to do.  Naturally, there is a superb view from the bridge and in the spring sunshine the whole strait looked very benign.  I asked about operating in poor weather, and was told that only rarely are ferries cancelled.  Mainly this happens in fog, not in rough weather.

Eventually I asked about the Sandettie Light, but this was met with blank looks.  I pointed to the chart and its position, but our course was well to the south of it, and would remain so.  I asked if the return journey would follow the same route and was assured that it would.  Then I mentioned weather forecasts, and one of the officers thought they had heard the BBC forecast, but a long time ago.  Weather is vital to the ferry service, particularly entering and leaving the docks, but the BBC twice daily forecast does not meet their needs. They get Navtext transmissions hourly, and detailed reports of current weather conditions from the ports of departure and arrival. We scanned the horizon checking for the characteristic flash, every 5 seconds, of the light. Despite being within the theoretical visibility range of the light, 24 miles, in the haze generated by the early spring sunshine, we could see nothing. In what seemed no time at all, it was time for me to say my thanks to the slightly bemused staff, and to leave the bridge to re-join my bike for disembarkation.

I had allowed myself a couple of hours ashore, and headed off to follow the signposts for the nearby Auchun supermarket to buy my cheese and wine. Now, many places on the Continent have enviable cycle tracks. We have cycled far and wide, in Holland, Germany and Denmark, enjoying the superb cycling provisions. But there was no such provision here. The road from the port was only just wide enough for two trucks to pass, and there were many scary encounters before I decided it was much safer to cycle along the rough grass verge. At last I bounced off the grass and on to the relative safety of a district road through the quiet village of Loon Plage. Though posted as a Dover-Dunkirk service, the actual ferry terminal is well to the west of Dunkirk, within a new industrial area. All around are canals, railways and chemical plants emitting smoke and flames to cloud the spring sky. Loon Plage is the nearest town of any size, though itself a long way from Dunkirk.

One French hypermarket is very much like another and I have yet to find a Gallic version of Waitrose. The fare on offer always seems quite at odds with French aspirations to be the culinary capital of the world. Especially in port areas, there are the inevitable rows of cheap beer and wine, and, particularly galling for the French, much of the cheap wine on offer is designed for British tastes, and so comes from Australia. Being neither a wine snob, nor particularly knowledgeable I settled for something safe from Bordeaux and a couple of reasonably ripe-smelling Camembert. I had no room for anything else.  When I planned the trip I had imagined I might have time for a leisurely French lunch, but that was not to be.  I ended up with a 'croque' and a gulped beer at the hypermarket snack-bar instead.  My dreams of finding a little Cafe-Restaurant had evaporated in the dismal Loon Plage main street.

To return to the port, I opted for a route through the industrial area, mainly to try to avoid the fight with the trucks on the port road. Instead I had to fight the wind and brave the fumes from the refinery chimneys, but I did at least arrive at the terminal without feeling I had diced with death too many times.  Checking-in, I was informed that my sailing was running an hour or more late, so I would have had time for a leisurely lunch, if only I had found somewhere to buy it.  Being a freight terminal, there was little in the way of facilities, certainly nothing to compensate for my missed lunch.  But I had my book, and so settled down in a quiet corner with a cup of machine tea to await departure.

British customs and immigration formalities are now carried out before embarkation; the better, it seems, to deter unwanted migrants.  I was surprised at the sophistication of the searches, and the equipment in use.  Since I clearly had nowhere to hide anything, never mind anybody, I sped through this hurdle. However, the next hurdle was not so easily overcome.  Unlike the Dover attendants who took my cycling in their stride, here the lady directing the traffic aboard was completely fazed by my appearance on a bike.  She shouted that I must wait out of the way, as it was dangerous to be amongst the trucks.  I could only agree. Outside the port I had no choice but to keep out of the way.  Here I had expected some assistance.  Eventually, a supervisor appeared and led me aboard while confessing he had never seen a cyclist use the service before.

By the time we cleared the port it was getting dark, and I spent a good part of the return journey scanning the horizon, again hoping to see the flashes from Sandettie, but to no avail.  Clearly she would take a little more persuading to give up her secrets.  Initially there seemed to be some mystery about her nationality. Is she British or French? A search on the web reveals that a Sandettie Lightship is moored in Dunkirk Harbour. I emailed Trinity House, the authority which maintains lighthouses and navigation buoys for English waters. In response, I received confirmation that the lightship is British, belongs to Trinity House and is indeed the weather station I was seeking. But further details would have to wait until I could make a successful visit.

My train journey home was as uneventful as the one out. By a stroke of good luck, I even managed to avoid all the stairs, and arrived home tired but content with my day, planning other expeditions. Another attempt to reach Sandettie would have to wait. I would have to find a surer method of reaching it.

# Bridlington

54° 6′ N          0° 10′ W

South southeast 3, 16 miles, 1006, Rising slowly

May 2005

After the disappointment of my first attempt to reach the Sandetti Light Vessel on a cross-channel ferry, I needed a success to keep my faith in the project alive. Bridlington seemed an ideal challenge. After all, it's a shore based weather station with a train station close by. It would be just the ticket. As luck would have it, while I was thinking about the trip, a review appeared in the Guardian for 'Audrey's Fish and Chip Shop' in Bridlington. Now, I am not a believer in cosmic coincidences but I do believe that every bit of information has its value. It seems that Audrey's is something of a legend in the Fish 'n' Chip world, so this choice morsel of information was tucked away to use later. In fact, on the basis of the review, it seemed that Audrey's would be sufficient of a draw to merit a visit to Bridlington on its own. But my plans were somewhat more complicated.

Checking the longitude and latitude I had for the weather station, I found it to be pleasingly close to Flamborough Head, which was probably the location of the original weather and coastguard station. The Head would have been an ideal place to hoist Fitzroy's weather signals, but I can find no confirmation of this. Although this is quite a walk from the train station, it was well within the bounds of an afternoon outing, and so I decided to use this as a route to approach the weather station itself. A little local research suggested a bus service to Bempton or to Flamborough itself would deposit us in the right area. Leaving the bus, we could join the coastal path, round the spectacular headland and see the weather station as we returned to Bridlington. If the famous Yorkshire weather permitted, it could be a very good outing. Evening, with fish and chips, in Bridlington would round off the day nicely.

On this occasion, I had been able to persuade my lady love to accompany me, lured by the prospect of the seaside, a coastal walk and a chance to explore a part of Yorkshire unknown to either of us. She is endlessly sympathetic to my eccentric travel ideas, but is also quite firm on which of these she will accompany me and which she will not. But, since it was my idea for the trip, it was down to me to make the arrangements too. I checked several times on web sites for train times and fares. How easy that is now. I remember trying to do similar things with a printed timetable, and in fact many of my colleagues from my railway days prided themselves on their abilities with the massive tome that was the British Railways published timetable. I had only to suggest a possible journey and someone would whip out a well thumbed timetable and reel off times with possible changes. Most likely they would be able to add some choice tit-bit about the construction or operation of that part of the railway. I never reached that level of proficiency, but always bought a current timetable, even long after I had left the railways. Nowadays, getting times from the web is simple, but instead there is a complete jumble of fares and charges from different sites, so regular checking usually pays. However, when we each had the required couple of days available, and I went to book, all the cheapest tickets had gone! Never mind, the fare I did manage to find still seemed good value, so we packed our overnight bags and set off.

Needing an early start (it seems we always do…) we boarded a train to London, then at King's Cross a smart GNER train for Doncaster. It was pleasant, fast and comfortable. In fact, none of the trains we took was late, and all the connections worked well. As an ex-railwayman, I hear many tales of woe about our railways, and frequently make myself unpopular by defending them. It seems everyone has heard of someone who has had the most awful experience, but I have to say, I see great improvements. Good news, of course, is no news, so we read little of these improvements. While I have had my own problems with train travel in the UK, the same is true for almost any railway system I have ever used. I could even tell tales of Swiss trains running late and stopping short of their destinations, tales rarely believed but true.

Not for the last time on my coastal stations quest was I able revel in the luxury of a comfortable seat, a good newspaper and an acceptable coffee, to say nothing of the company and the countryside through which we sped. Arriving on schedule at Doncaster, we had time for another coffee, then boarded a single coach train which took us via Hull to Bridlington. Predictably, this was altogether a more utilitarian vehicle, basic but functional, municipal rather than metropolitan. It gave a suitable impression of an entry vehicle to more neglected parts of the country. And so it turned out when we arrived at Hull. The station has certainly seen better days. In its heyday it must have been very grand indeed, but it seems that where once there was a vast and busy terminal there is now little but parked cars. There should be a better use for such a building, but neglect is evident. No doubt the fish trains, along with the fish, are long gone too.

In contrast the station at Bridlington is a delight. The essentials of the old station have been retained in a sensitive refurbishment. The ticket office looks original, and the station bar/buffet is warm and welcoming, loaded with railway bric-a-brac. Amazing what a little imagination can do, along with a little money to carry out some careful modernisations. I'm pretty sure the result is attractive to more than the odd coach load of train passengers, and seems well patronised. At any rate, it was a welcoming sight for us, and led our thoughts well away from the visions of neglect we had been pondering earlier in the journey.

The sun was shining as we walked into the town, looking for the tourist office. English seaside towns have a logic, or lack of logic, of their own. Not so much faded glory as fashions apart. A warm sunny day should have brought out the fun seekers, but wherever we looked there were few who seemed to be having fun. Older people mostly wore a look of tired resignation along with too many clothes. Younger people seemed disproportionately represented by big girls, bare midriffs bulging over too tight trousers, pushing toddlers in buggies and puffing smoke in the air. The smell of the sea, and of the seaside – warm chip fat! – wafted up from the sea front. But horror of horrors, the warm chip fat did not emanate from Audrey's. Just our luck to pick a day when Audrey closed her shop, though the Guardian article suggested she opens every day. We would have to choose another establishment, of which there were many, for our evening meal. But that challenge could wait till later; we had other fish to fry in the meantime.

First stop, the tourist office where, anticipating a late return to the town, we quickly booked our lodgings, then the bus station, to take the bus to North Landing, just round the coast from Flamborough Head. But somewhere on the outskirts of the town, the little bus seemed to run out of puff. Cautiously the driver parked up, and apologised. There would be a slight delay, he said, as he needed to fix a problem which had seemed to recur occasionally. Before he did so, he needed to report to base, but his phone battery was dead! Fearing an extended delay while he looked for a phone box and the loss of our walking time, I offered him my phone to call in, and hopefully get moving again quickly. He gratefully accepted, and not many minutes later we were on our way again.

The walk around the head is beautiful.  Gorse was out, seabirds nested on the limestone cliffs, swooping and calling over the calm clear sea.  In the distance, the lighthouse showed clear against the blue sky.  North Landing itself is home to one of the area's two lifeboats.    Originally these were based on either side of Flamborough Head, one on the north, the other at, where else, South Landing.  This ensured that one would always be to the lee side of the Head, and so could launch pretty much whatever the weather.  Later, as technology advanced, the South Landing station was moved in to Bridlington town, by the beach.

Just above the lifeboat station, where the cliff-top path turned a sharp corner, one of the house owners had laid out a series of painted placards with what must be the world's worst jokes.  Sample:- 'Three things tell you your (sic) getting old, Loss of Memory and I forget what the other two things are'.  Bemused at first, around the corner we saw a collecting box for Yorkshire Cancer Research.  'There's now't as strange as folk,' as they are rumoured to say in these parts.

A little further along the way, we came across a reminder of a largely forgotten episode from the past.  A memorial mentioned a sea battle between John Paul Jones and a Royal Navy frigate off the headland in 1779 during the American War of Independence.  Little was said of the fighting itself, but later research showed that it was an epic sea battle fought in Britain's home waters.  The result was that John Paul Jones, despite apparently overwhelming odds of size and armament against him, captured the British ship *Serapis*.  His own ship, *Bonhomme Richard*, suffered terrible damage in the encounter that resulted in it sinking soon after the *Serapis* surrendered.  In a twist of fate more reminiscent of Hollywood than the real world of naval warfare, Jones transferred his men and his command to the *Serapis* and continued his voyage.

Intrigued by this story, I researched further and found out that John Paul Jones was a complex character, feted in the USA, ignored or worse in Britain. Born John Paul in Scotland, he went to sea very young, working at first on ships, including slavers, trading between West Africa, the West Indies and Britain. Later he was involved in a fight that resulted in him killing one or possibly two crew members. The circumstances are unclear but he changed his name in order to settle in the Colonies, where an older brother was already established. In those days seamen frequently changed their names or gave false names when signing on to merchant ships, as a way to hide their past.

However, the year was 1774, and this may not have been a great time to try to settle down peacefully in Virginia as a farmer, and Jones' temperament may not have been suited to the life of a plantation owner. War between Britain and her American colonies loomed. Whether from a new found patriotism for his newfound homeland, problems on the plantation, or because he feared British victory would result in British justice catching up with him, he decided to offer his services to the navy being formed by the Continental Congress. But he got involved in a series of disputes, and became disillusioned with his new employers. Perhaps to get him out of the way, or to keep him out of trouble, he was sent to France to try to bring their navy to the assistance of the United States of America. Here he met and worked with Benjamin Franklin and John Adams, and together they planned raids on British shipping and coastal towns.

He proved very good at this, sinking ships and taking prizes back to France, but was unlucky in some of his more spectacular endeavours. An attack on Whitehaven harbour, with the intention of setting fire to some of the two to three hundred ships sheltering there, failed because his plan was discovered. A plan to kidnap the Earl of Selkirk, to exchange for captured American sailors, failed because the Earl was away when Jones came calling. At that time, the British government treated all American naval sailors as pirates, terrorists in fact, and as so they were liable to be executed. Having some means to ransom fellow sailors was of great importance to their colleagues. For this reason, John Paul Jones himself is frequently described as an 'American Pirate' in British descriptions of the sea war, right up to the present day.

The Battle of Flamborough Head was undoubtedly a feat of considerable heroism, and is celebrated as such, with much hyperbole[1]. Check any American web site for information on the man called 'The Founder of the American Navy' and ascribed the highest of motives and abilities. He is credited with establishing 'the traditions of courage and professionalism that the sailors of the United States Navy today proudly maintain[2].' He is widely said to have replied "I have not yet begun to fight!" when challenged to surrender by the British commander though, as with many famous quotes, it appears these words were first written down some forty-five years later.

After the Flamborough Head battle, Jones eluded other British patrol ships and sailed to Holland. While the battle was the pinnacle of Jones' naval career, in the period after the battle Jones demonstrated considerable shortcomings. He seems to have been very vain and concerned mainly with his reputation. The Flamborough Head victory gave him considerable glory in which he revelled. Arriving in Amsterdam he was received as a hero and he played to his newfound admirers, a celebrity of his age. He worked hard to publicise his own fame, writing dozens of letters, giving interviews, and getting accounts of the battle published in newspapers. While this publicity helped further the American cause, Jones focused on it to the detriment of his command, neglecting his crew and their own valiant part in the battle. He was said to be slow to credit subordinates or superiors and quick to criticize them. As a result, he comes across as ungrateful and self-absorbed, not at all the paragon of virtue claimed by legend in the USA.

The commitment to professional standards and training, much vaunted by his later fans, seems at odds with his loss of the ship on which he was to return to America. The circumstances were something close to mutiny. Instead of sailing as instructed, Jones spent time in Paris, living the life of the conquering hero. A letter to Jones from his patron and friend Benjamin Franklin is revealing[3]. Franklin wrote: "If you had stayed on board where your duty lay, instead of coming to Paris, you would not have lost your ship... hereafter, if you should observe an occasion to give your officers and friends a little more praise than is their due, and confess more fault than you can justly be charged with, you will only become the sooner for it, a great captain. Criticizing and censuring almost every one you have to do with, will diminish friends, increase enemies, and thereby hurt your affairs." The officers decided to sail as scheduled and returned to America without him.

The exploits of John Paul Jones have entered mythology in America, and been largely forgotten here in Britain. His final naval assignments, however, were not fighting for his adopted country, nor against the 'auld enemy'. Following the end of the American War of Independence, Jones was recruited into the Russian Navy, then at war with Turkey. But it seems his difficulties with his fellow officers again caused trouble and he was recalled to St. Petersburg, where he complained of plots and intrigues against him by officers and Princes. Eventually he returned to France, but died of a brain tumour before he could return to America[4].

We hear little of encounters like this in our history, and often the version we read bears a decidedly slanted view of the events. A local Flamborough website suggests the following sequence of events;- 'In 1779, when two British naval ships engaged the American pirate, commodore John Paul Jones's fleet for over two hours, inflicting heavy losses and Jones's ship, *Bonhomme Richard*, is believed to have sunk after the battle to the north, just off Filey[5]. (sic)' No mention of the fate of the Royal Navy ships at all! Perhaps we should be reassured at the way that this war between two nations, now seemingly inseparable allies, has faded. Certainly there are many things about that conflict to be aghast at. Visitors to the White House are still shown treasures salvaged when it was burned by British troops, who, in a despicable act of vandalism, went on to burn the Library of Congress. Maybe it's just as well we forget them.

Continuing our coastal walk, we had a chance to remark on the very interesting geology of Flamborough Head. It is one of the most spectacular areas of chalk cliffs in Britain, rising 400 feet from the chilly North Sea and protruding several miles out from the general line of the coast. The chalk beds that make up the cliffs were laid down millions of years ago, at the time the last dinosaurs were still roaming the earth. Erosion reveals new fossils all the time.

Nowadays these cliffs are home to one of the largest sites of nesting sea birds in England, boasting a rare mainland colony of gannets. The steep cliffs and sea stacks provide a nesting area safe from the cats and rats that plague most areas near human habitation. Walking the cliff top path, something of a bird-watchers paradise, we were frequently 'buzzed' by wary parents, and had a splendid view of chicks calling loudly to their parents for food. Not all human contact is unwelcome to the nesting colony. Somehow, someone had placed a rubber tyre over the sharp pinnacle of a chalk sea stack. A very contented Great Blackback gull was ensconced in this techno-nest when we passed. Avian visitors to the headland reportedly include oyster catchers, many different types of gull, eider ducks, and cormorants. The chalk headland also provides favourable growing conditions for a wide variety of plant species, including orchids. Not being experts, we could only identify the more common varieties, and marvel at the profusion and colours of the wildflowers generally.

Approaching the head itself, we could see various aerials spread about and an old tower indicating the importance of this headland as a lookout point, now as well as in the past. At the lighthouse, there seemed scant evidence of a weather station ever having been here, though one or two instruments could be seen on the railings near the top. Visiting time was over, so we missed the chance to explore further, and to enquire of its possible history as one of Fitzroy's signal stations. Further down the road, an older coast guard station seemed similarly deserted. Many former coastguard cottages, and lighthouse keepers' cottages, are now available to rent as holiday lets. What used to be a lonely posting for the keepers of the coast are now viewed as suitable places to get away from it all. Such is progress. However, neither then nor later was I able to establish the credentials of the lighthouse or the coastguard station as a previous weather station. The earlier lighthouse tower, constructed of local chalk and stone, dates from the time of Charles II, indicating just how long trade vessels have depended on navigational beacons on landmarks such as Flamborough Head. Satisfied with our visit to the Head, but still curious about the local history, we departed and in the most wonderful evening light, continued our walk along the coast towards Bridlington.

On the edge of the town, just at the start of the promenade, where we had expected it to be, we at last came across the large new coastguard building, flags fluttering in the evening breeze. The garden was a profusion of metrological instruments, but there was no obvious place to knock and introduce ourselves. Luckily, as we debated a suitable course of action, we spotted a uniformed officer entering the building by way of a set of steps. We followed him up the stairs and found ourselves at the door of a large operations room, manned by about six smartly dressed coastguards, each at a bank of screens. This was to be the first of many occasions when I explained the quest which brought us to a weather station. Well, I mumbled what I hoped was enough not to have us ejected as undesirables. But I need not have worried, for we were warmly welcomed and shown around the operations room.

Looking at the vast display of technology, I felt the need to confirm that this was indeed the actual weather station. One of the officers explained that weather reporting was just one of the many duties performed by the station, in fact a small part of their work monitoring the sea and the shoreline. He showed us the various instruments used to record the weather, and their recording and reporting mechanisms. Mostly the instruments are automatic, but the weather log is still filled out by hand, and reported to the Met Office every hour.

Shortly after we arrived a weather report was due to be sent to the Met Office, so we watched as the officer collected readings from the instruments we had been exploring, and coded up the results in the big weather log book. Visibility is the one weather parameter still best established manually, not automatically. In this case, the reporting officer calculates visibility by recording whether or not certain landmarks are visible. The report sent included the following;-

Bridlington, South southeast 3, 1006, rising slowly, 16 miles

This should be interpreted as a light wind (force 3) from south-south east, pressure 1006 millibars (higher than 1000 and rising usually indicates good weather), with visibility of 16 nautical miles.

Transmission to the Met Office now consists of filling out an email, but of course in the distant past, telegraph would have been the only available route. However, that would have been long before the current building was constructed.

Having completed the 18:00 (GMT) Weather Report, we had a tour of the instruments in the garden. Some technology does not date. If you want to measure the rainfall, there is no substitute for having a rain gauge! In fact, much of the basic weather measurement technology would be immediately recognisable to any weather recorder from the last hundred years or more. The basic layout of a weather observatory has changed little in that time, and is repeated at each of the weather stations, here and abroad. However, alongside the traditional equipment, modern electronic instruments monitor and record readings silently. These form the basis of the readings sent to the Met Office, and so on to the BBC and the Shipping Forecast.

By now, evening had arrived, and we said our goodbyes to the friendly staff and continued into the town in search of the Fish 'n' Chips I had promised as the reward. Many many years ago, I visited the original Harry Ramsden's in Guiseley, long before it morphed into a fast food chain. That experience has always tainted my opinions of restaurants that serve fish and chips, as opposed to real Fish 'n' Chip restaurants. In those days, and maybe still, each item on Harry Ramsden's menu was accompanied by bread, butter and tea. There was no sign of a pie or a sausage or chicken. Curry sauce? Forget it, the only extras on offer were peas, or baked beans. Those still seem to me the marks of a true Fish 'n' Chip restaurant. With a little effort we found a reasonable establishment, with good fish and tasty chips, even mushy peas, but no bread and butter. In place of the tea, which was on offer, we chose beer, and were amused when this was served in cans, no glasses. Perhaps my standards are unrealistic, and perhaps it's just as well we didn't make it to Audrey's. Maybe it's better to keep that dream of a perfect Fish 'n' Chip place by the sea, and not put it to the test.

So, back to our lodgings, a good night's sleep and an early breakfast before reversing our journey of the day before. We were both well satisfied with our visit to the seaside, and the Bridlington Weather Station, with its various tales to tell. As often happens, the topic for discussion on the return journey was which one next and when? There was still a long way to go.

---

[1] See for example the biography of Jones included in 'Lives of Distinguished American Naval Officer's by J. Fenimore Cooper, published in 1846 and quoted on www.history.navy.mil/bios/jones_jp.htm.

[2] From 'John Paul Jones' another biography by Denis M Conrad quoted on www.history.navy.mil/bios/jones_jp.htm.

[3] Quoted in 'John Paul Jones' by Denis M Conrad as above.

[4] See John Paul Jones on Wikipedia.

[5] See www.flamboroughhead.co.uk/battle.html.

# Greenwich Light Vessel (Automatic)

50° 24′ N        0° 00′ W

West southwest 5, 12 miles, Fair, 1003 Rising

June 2007

Was this cheating, I asked myself again as I boarded a Lisbon bound plane at Heathrow. Strictly speaking, air travel should not come into my quest, but I claimed that this was different, not an exception. My excuse was that I was on my way to join the magnificent sailing bark, *Europa*[1], to sail back to Amsterdam. With any luck, and a little negotiation with the captain, I was hoping to achieve a double, Greenwich Light and the elusive Sandettie, as we progressed up the channel and through the Dover Straits. Ten days under sail aboard a traditional tallship seemed to justify the use of a plane to get to the starting point, Horta in the Azores. Actually, I could claim that I was 're-joining' after previously leaving the ship. In September 2000 I first stepped aboard her, having travelled by train and ferry to Bremerhaven, and later joined her for a voyage to Antarctica. But that's a bit too tenuous!

Theoretically, I could have made my way over land and sea, at least to Lisbon, but then I would be stuck. As there is no regular ferry service to the Azores, I would have needed to take a plane from there, or spend a lot more time than I had, trying to talk myself aboard a freighter.   So I stuck to my justification, flew to the starting point and sailed the clipper route back to Europe.

In starting my own voyage in the Azores, I was to cross paths with my old 'friends', James Cook and Robert Fitzroy, and find out some interesting links between the Azores and weather forecasting.  But more of that later.  The Azores would have been a regular stopping place for the trade wind sailors in the great days of sail.  Nowadays, Horta has a well deserved reputation as the stopping place of other sailors, yachtsmen setting out to cross the Atlantic in search of sun and adventure in the Caribbean, or further west still.  Most leave a memento of their crossing inscribed on the quay.  As a result, almost every available surface is covered with colourfully painted motifs of the yachts and ships, with the names of their sailors. *Europa*'s crew update and refresh theirs on each visit, now usually twice a year as she heads south to Antarctica for the austral summer and returns north for maintenance.  Indeed, I was fortunate enough to sail aboard her to Antarctica in January 2003. On that occasion I joined the ship at Ushuaia, in Tierra del Fuego having explored more connections with Robert Fitzroy.

While Charles Darwin explored ashore, Fitzroy pursued the arduous task of charting the treacherous waters which formed the shipping channels around Cape Horn.  Some of his survey work still appears on current charts.   In fact, Fitzroy's journey with Darwin was the second voyage of the *Beagle* to those waters, and Fitzroy's second charting expedition.  He first visited Tierra del Fuego in 1829, and 'acquired' four Fuegians after an incident in which a ship's boat was stolen.  Having brought them to Europe, to be 'civilised', Fitzroy felt an obligation to return them, and *Beagle*'s second voyage was originally planned as a private venture to do so. Fitzroy was a wealthy man, and had considerable resources at his disposal, though such an expedition would have been very costly, and as a private venture, much less ambitious.  Fortunately, he found a sponsor at the Admiralty, Admiral Beaufort, and was able to equip the now famous mission.  One of the Fuegians died in England, but the others, named by Fitzroy as Jemmy Button,

Fuegian Basket and York Minster, travelled on the *Beagle*, and were duly returned to their native land.    Perhaps predictably, two quickly re-integrated into their own culture, much to the dismay of Fitzroy.    More tragically the third captive, Jemmy Button, lived out his life in between his two worlds, scanning the horizon for visiting ships and contact with Europe, and partly ostracised by his compatriots.

To get to the Azores I had to start early, and as the alarm went off, from the depths of my slumber, I caught the Shipping Forecast. How appropriate, on two counts!  I snuggled up to my lady love and listened for Biscay and Fitzroy.   S to SW, force 3-5, high pressure building – it sounded perfect sailing weather for my voyage.  At Lisbon, I changed planes and we headed out over Sea Area Trafalgar. The cloud formations below did not seem quite as benevolent as the Forecast had suggested.   So it was, as we descended through the clouds, buffeted by a strong wind, and wobbled in for a bumpy landing on Horta.

For consolation, there was the wonderful sight of *Europa*, soon to be my ship, in the bay below.  She looked very inviting, swinging gently on her anchor, and occasionally leaning before the Atlantic gusts.  Later, I learned that she was anchored almost exactly where Captain Cook had anchored *Resolution* on the return journey from his second voyage.  Cook, ever the innovator, had waited until he was approaching the Azores and nearly home to try out a distillation system to produce drinking water from the sea[2].  He was pleased with its success and recommended that future voyages be equipped with this device as a safety measure, and to avoid the need to stop in unfamiliar locations if water ran low.

Perhaps on this recommendation the *Bounty* was so equipped for her fateful voyage, though it seems not to have been used to alleviate the apparent shortage of water aboard.   However, the mutineers who took *Bounty* to Pitcairn did put the still to a very different use, and produced a creditable spirit from the roots of the tee tree. Their resulting heavy drinking seems to have accounted for at least some of the murders and deaths that ensued after their landing. It was while seriously drunk that John Adams, the sole mutineer to survive until rescue, had a 'religious' experience that resulted in the re-shaping of the community which enabled it to survive.

Fitzroy and Darwin also came to the Azores on the *Beagle* as they returned from the famous voyage. It is probable that Fitzroy called in on other occasions, given the need to re-supply on either the outward or return legs of his long journeys. He would have no doubt been pleased to see the establishment of a weather station here in Horta, though some time after he had established his own around Britain. It seems that no less a figure than Prince Albert of Monaco, taking a Princely interest in the weather, decided to take advantage of the transatlantic cable that stopped off here. As an amateur scientist, he recognised that much of Europe's weather came from the Atlantic. Quite possibly his interest was kindled by the work Fitzroy and others had done on weather forecasting in Northern Europe and he saw the possibility of repeating this further south. After a well publicised visit he endowed a weather station that still bears his name.

Darwin observed, on finally leaving Brazil for the Azores – "I thank God that I shall never again visit a slave-country" and went on to revile the slave trade, still in existence across the South Atlantic, and the keeping of slaves – still legal in the United States as well as Brazil.[3] He had famously rowed with Fitzroy on the subject, but his arguments must have struck home for later in the voyage Fitzroy's journal records thoughts of using his own resources to fund, and possibly lead, a 'privateer' to tackle the south Atlantic slave trade.

When the appointed day to board *Europa* arrives, with my friend Mary from many voyages, we are ferried out from the marina, past the hundreds of painted visiting cards. On board, there are old hands and new. Joining a ship is always accompanied by some apprehension. Will the old hands, having been together some time, be willing and able to share their ship? How will they welcome us strangers? Will it come as a surprise to them that some new faces are in fact old hands? As any situation where old and new mix, there are a variety of reactions. Once we set sail however, and the watches are organised, all except the newly seasick will begin to feel at home, and gradually a team will form. And so we hope to be for the remaining days of our voyage together, for now it really becomes our ship. From here on, you might say we are all in the same boat.

After some refresher training in the ways of the ship, we weigh anchor, leave the shelter of the island and move out into the ocean swell. Soon we are heeled over at about 15 degrees, and remain that way for pretty much the rest of the voyage. The angle varies constantly, down to 10 and up to 20 or so, but it is always there, courtesy of the ocean swell and the fine sailing breeze that sweeps us along at a respectable speed, day and night.

Living at this angle has its challenges. Just walking along the deck for a start, or standing still. Mind you, it is great for the muscle tone as you exercise lots of muscles all the time. Even sitting still, bracing this way and that, pushing yourself back along a seat, it is all exercise. Similarly with standing. There is no standing still. You constantly adjust your sway, left and right, and then a big swell makes the ship jump from under you and you must catch hold or fall over.

Imagine the challenge of eating. The rule is one hand for the ship and one for your food, but one for the ship barely suffices. Consider breakfast. The cooks have laid out an inviting spread, muesli, yoghurt, bread, butter, ham, cheese, eggs, fruit and lots more beside. To aspirant sailors, being also aspirant gluttons, this spread is a real test. The experts gather breakfast in stages, first muesli, then coffee, then juice. The impatient try one thing too many. A hand taken from a glass of juice frequently sees the contents fly across the table. Which is another lesson from the experts: try to sit on the uphill side of the table, then your spills will not land in your own lap, and you will avoid the spills of your messmates.

If you managed breakfast, you may fancy a shower. The shower room has a completely new set of challenges. Where will the water land as it flows from the shower? Important, since it starts cold. Personally, I find sitting on the loo to take a shower very effective. And the tap above the basin, as you do your teeth? Will the water hit the basin, or the floor? Other challenges in the shower room I leave to your imagination.

At sea, we are rarely without companions from the animal world. Probably dolphins are the most special ocean wildlife we encounter, because they choose to come to us, to make the effort to see and to be seen. They take time off from their daily chores to cast a curious eye over the ship, then experiment near the bow - pushing and jostling as children do on a school outing. Then, just as suddenly as they arrived, they are gone.

Most frequently visible are shearwaters, distant cousins of the more famous albatross. Perhaps albatross have better public relations agents, or it may be that their more impressive size accounts for their being better known. None the less shearwaters behave in a similar fashion. They are beautiful flyers, effortlessly wheeling and skimming the rolling swell, riding the winds, rarely flapping a wing. They are superbly adapted for a life on the ocean.

Similarly well adapted are the tiny petrels we see flitting between the rollers, dodging the surf. At first glance they seem like lost land birds, dipping their feet occasionally into the water. But this impression is deceptive, for they are truly ocean birds. 'Storm Petrel' is the name given to one such species, for the only time they were encountered was when some battered body was cast ashore following a great storm at sea.

From time to time we crowd on deck at the shout of 'Whales!' but usually all we see is their moist breath above the waves. We are not skilled enough to tell from their 'blow' what kind they are and they do not come, like their distant dolphin cousins, to examine us. So we pass, curious; they just pass.

We know there are fish aplenty nearby too, but despite our efforts with a troll line, none comes to dinner. Small consolation that Capt. Cook suffered similar failure, bemoaning in his log that they caught very little as 'we were such bad fishers[4]'. Perhaps we should be content that we leave the fish for the dolphins.

Having set the sails, and in the steady southwest trade winds, there is not much sail handling to do. Occasionally the watch officer will decide to brace the yards which hold the square sails: moving them a few degrees to port or starboard, or to replace one of the sails with a larger or a smaller one. Then there is much frantic activity for a few minutes before the normal rhythm reasserts itself. Some sailors pass the daylight hours reading, writing journals or playing cards. Others join in the general maintenance tasks of the ship.

Of course, in the days of the trading ships, sailors would not have had the option as to how to pass their time. Keeping a sailing bark shipshape is a constant headache; endless maintenance is required, a sort of sea-going equivalent of painting the Forth Bridge. I was lucky to find among the crew another expatriate Irishman, Thomas, who had some considerable experience at sea and was willing to allow me to assist with a few of the maintenance tasks. Thomas explained some details of the standing rigging, and together we climbed the foremast and set about replacing and repairing some of the lines that keep the ship seaworthy. By climbing out on the yard, and hanging over the billowing sail, we were able to work reasonably comfortably. This was a small triumph for me, but unfortunately a drop in the ocean of the mate's seemingly endless maintenance task list.

Other distractions are less physically demanding. We boarded *Europa* and set sail on 15th June, well before the summer solstice and the longest day. Sailors, lacking other sources of stimulation debate even trivia endlessly, so it was no surprise when the subject of the longest day came up for discussion. Surely everyone knows that 21st June is the longest day, but is that always so? Travelling north at this time of year, the days obviously get longer the further north you go. If you doubt this, just consider what would happen if you went from London to Tromso, north of the Arctic circle. So, for us northbound sailors, the 21st June may not be the longest day! I started a discussion with fellow voyagers over breakfast as to when our longest day would in fact be. Clearly for all, 21st June is the summer solstice, and each day after the solstice will be shorter at each location in the northern hemisphere. The question is, by how much will each day shorten, and as we make progress north, for us, by how much will each day lengthen? And when will the two balance out?

Many opinions were expressed. Some were dubious of the whole concept, others insisting the 21st June had to be the longest day. Still others were amused at the idea, but doubted that our increasing northern latitude would make much difference. And then again others commented on how much earlier the sun rose as we paced the decks during our night watches, only to be contradicted on the grounds that we had been heading about ENE for a week. We had changed time zones, but had not altered the ship's clock. No one seemed to remember what time the sun set, perhaps because the bar opened before dinner, and closed very late into the night.

I was pretty sure I knew the solution and was willing to open a book on the result, but there were few takers. Fortunately being aboard ship, the library contained a current nautical almanac so in theory the answer should be easily found. The results were as I suspected, but the magnitudes surprised me. In the latitudes of our voyage, 40 to 50 degrees north, the day-length changes by only about a second between 21st and 22nd of June. And in the week either side of the solstice, the day-length varies only by a few seconds. Imagine the problems faced by the original builders of Stonehenge. How would they decide on the day that was to be the actual longest day?    Particularly if there were clouds on the horizon?    A similar problem faced the builders of the famous Newgrange mound in Ireland, which is oriented for the shortest day.  It's no surprise that the ancients seem not to have recognised the equinoxes. They had no means to measure the length of a day or night.

But the other part of the puzzle depended on finding out how much longer each day is as you travel north.   On 21st June at the Tropic of Cancer the day will be pretty much 12 hours long, while at the Arctic Circle it will be 24 hours long.  So there is a transition, but it would be a mistake to assume this is at a steady rate.  Again, the almanac provided the answer, in terms of the difference between the times of sunrise and sunset at different latitudes.  In our latitudes, around the summer solstice, the day lengthens by about 12 minutes for each degree north we travel.  Again I was surprised at the magnitude, but debating the calculations provided plenty of distraction in the bar each evening.

So there we have the solution to the problem of determining our longest day.  It would be the day on which we reached our furthest north, that is, the day we would arrive home to Amsterdam.

The voyage was a wonderful opportunity to savour the gradual transitions no longer common when most of our travels involve the brutal dislocation of air travel.  Of course, the transition from land to sea on leaving was pretty swift too.  Though not in the middle of the Atlantic Ocean, the Azores are on the Mid-Atlantic Ridge, where the sea floor is spreading east and west, driving Europe and America further apart at about the speed at which your fingernails grow.  The transition from land to deep ocean is swift, steep basalt cliffs plunging to the ocean floor, and sheltered anchorage giving way to ocean swell within an hour of sailing.

But subsequent transitions are more gentle.  Nearing England, we see subtle changes in the ocean wildlife.  The shearwaters no longer stream past on the waves.  Instead, we see gannets on patrol, prepared to dive at speed should they spy a meal below. Their Pacific cousins, the boobies, have always been harbingers of land to the Polynesian seafarers. Where shearwaters spend a long time at sea, gannets (and boobies) return to roost on land most nights, so if you encounter them on a voyage, follow them as the sun begins to set and you will find land!

The ocean itself undergoes a quite dramatic transition too. Over the space of about 50 miles, the ocean floor rises from depths of 4000 metres and more to around 100 metres as we cross onto the continental shelf. We first became aware of this as we encountered fishing vessels in the night, working the edge of the shelf. Next we noticed the absence of the ocean swell, for the first time since we left Horta. The relatively shallow water of the continental shelf absorbs the energy of the waves, decreasing their height and power.

In the deep ocean, we saw little sight of other users of the sea. Now we find shipping all around. We are entering some of the busiest shipping lanes of the world, so the lookouts are given renewed instructions. With the shipping come other signs that land is close by. We see the beam of a distant lighthouse, Bishop Rock, just west of Scilly, sweep the low clouds, visible evidence of the dangers that land presents to vessels such as ours. It is readily identified by its characteristic flashes, two every 15 seconds, visible for about 24 nautical miles.

Sailing up the English Channel, I might have expected to see the Channel Light Vessel, my first Coastal Station, again. But the channel is really quite wide at this point, and our course kept us well away from the middle, the preserve of major shipping vessels speeding to and from the ports of Europe. The Channel Light Vessel is almost in the centre of the English Channel marking the start of one of the traffic separation zones. Though its light may be visible from many miles away, we were well beyond its range. I just had to hope that we would be nearer to my real quarry, the Greenwich Lightship.

If the transitions in the world around us are gentle, perhaps the transition for the crew is slightly less so. As we sight land, we receive mobile phone signals and contact with home and family is quickly re-established. Now talk turns to life on land, to timetables and commitments beyond the next watch. Soon many will be swept up in the now unfamiliar haste of airports and railway stations again, looking back to a rich experience shared.

For the clipper ships sailing this route in the great days of sail, sight of land would not necessarily mean home was just around the corner. 'To Falmouth for Orders' was the sailing instruction given to the masters of most trade ships. Their cargos might be bought and sold several times while they were at sea, sometimes the vessel too. Arriving off Falmouth, ships received their new orders as to where to deliver their cargo, perhaps to Hamburg or Stockholm, maybe back to Spain. Home could still be a long way off.

For me though, there would be no new orders. I was looking forward to the crux of the voyage as regards to the 'Coastal Stations' quest. We were bearing down on the Greenwich meridian and with it the Greenwich Light Vessel (automatic). Having had great sailing winds all the way from Horta, we were now becalmed off the Isle of Wight. Should this continue, we would be forced to motor, and thus be obliged to use the Traffic Separation Zones in the channel. Sailing vessels use the Inshore Traffic Zone reserved for coastal shipping, but only if they are sailing! In order to use the Separation Zone, we would need to cross within a short distance of the Greenwich Light, which marks the midpoint of its south-western extremity. Eastbound traffic must use the southern side of the zone. If we sailed, we would be on the north of the westbound lane, further away from the Light. Either way, based on current progress, we would pass it in the hours of darkness. Though I wanted to sail, perhaps secretly I was hoping that we would motor, and get a clearer view of my quarry.

It was late at night when I came on deck to check on progress, and the engine had been quiet for some hours. The duty watch had re-set the sails as the wind freshened from the west, and we were making a steady 7.5 knots. Our course was east northeast, heading towards Newhaven to join the Inshore Traffic Zone along the south coast of England. We must have looked a fine sight to anyone who was awake on the vast bulk of the QM2 as she steamed quickly by, heading for her home port, Southampton.

In the wheelhouse, I consulted the chart and looked at the GPS. We had about 11 miles to go before we crossed the prime meridian, so it would be about half an hour before I could expect to see the tell-tale flash of the lightship, as we made our closest approach to it. I checked the radar, expecting to see the 'RACON' (from RAdar beaCON) identifier transmitted by the lightship in response to our radar sweep. But it was nowhere to be seen. I called the watch officer, fearing that I had miscalculated something. Fortunately he quickly remembered that a Coast Guard bulletin earlier in the night had announced that the 'RACON' was not functioning due to a defect, and warning shipping to take care. He confirmed my calculations, and we looked out toward the south-east, checking the horizon for the light.

Although the chart gives a theoretical distance from which the light should be visible, 21 miles, this can obviously be affected by weather conditions. Low cloud can, paradoxically, make the light visible from further away, as the sweep of the beam illuminates the underside of the clouds. Pretty soon, this is exactly what we saw, and as we drew closer we could make out the beam, with its characteristic flash, on the horizon, 5 seconds lit followed by 5 seconds dark. But in the pitch black night, could I really claim to have seen the vessel? Undaunted, I set off to climb up the main mast to the platform, 20 metres above the deck, to get the best view possible. Going aloft on a tallship is a wonderful experience, but a challenge. In the dark, the challenge is magnified, but so is the reward. In the dark, all the handholds and balance points you have learned in daylight are invisible, so you work by touch alone.

Experience counts and fortunately I had had plenty of opportunity to practise during my maintenance work with Thomas. Best not to try this for the first time at night! I swung onto the platform, turned to look south and there was my reward, the light was clearly visible, standing above the horizon, and flashing out its message to the surrounding shipping. What automatic weather

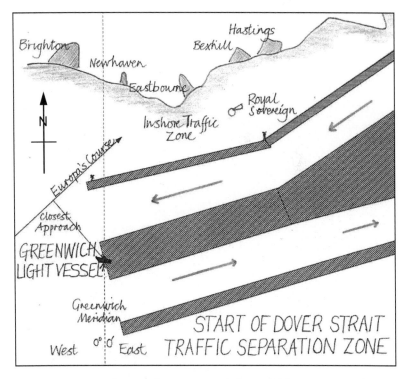

report was it sending at that moment? I would have to wait for my return to find out from the friendly Met Office web site.

This gave the following report:-

West southwest 5, 12 miles, Fair, 1003 Rising

Descending to the deck, and returning to the wheelhouse, I resumed my conversation with the watch officer, while keeping an eye on the GPS. We had passed our closest encounter with the Greenwich Lightship before we crossed the magic 0 degrees longitude, due to our northeasterly course. Now we were racing towards the prime meridian, and I wanted to watch the dial trip over as we moved from the western to the eastern hemisphere. A childish pursuit I know, but almost compulsive, like watching the odometer of a car click over the tens of thousands. My companion confessed to a similar compulsion, but as the seconds of longitude approached zero, and I began a loud countdown, he continued telling me of his plans ashore, not glancing at the GPS display. My announcement of 'zero' elicited no nod of recognition, so I returned to the conversation, and some minutes later announced my intention to go below again. Only then did he look at the GPS, while inquiring whether or not I would be back for the 'transition'. Recognition dawned, followed by a comment that he now knew why I had been behaving rather oddly, counting down while he talked! I went below to bed.

The coastguard bulletin we received in the morning, as we dodged the ferries in warm sunlight outside Dover harbour, warned of coming northwesterly gales, and of a malfunction on the elusive Sandettie Light. Its visibility was temporarily reduced to 12 miles. It mattered not to us as we continued sailing slowly up the English coast. We were well outside its possible range of visibility in daylight, and, to weather the coming storm, the captain had decided to sail north throughout the day. This course would take us well away from the normal shipping lanes, and the hazards of commercial traffic. Sandettie would remain elusive for the moment.

The voyage however, had one last surprise. North from Dover, its white cliffs bathed in sunlight, we followed a little used, though well marked, channel through the notorious Goodwin Sands. All day, in the balmy sunshine, we sailed sedately north, crossing the mouth of the Thames Estuary and then along the low-lying coasts of Essex and Suffolk. The gentle breeze wafted us along at a steady 2 – 3 knots but often progress seemed to depend more on tide than wind. Towards sunset we saw dark clouds building ahead, inland and away from the coast. But there could be little doubt they were heading our way. The forecast northwesterly gales could not be far off. At midnight, as the watch changed, so did the weather. We tacked hurriedly, setting a new course to run before the gale, east and home to Amsterdam.

Overnight the wind built to Severe Gale Force 9 and we lurched violently in our bunks below. Sleep was impossible for longer than snatched catnaps. On deck, there was a complete 'lock-down'. Deadlights covered the deckhouse windows. Watertight doors to the deck were secured. Safety lines guarded the poop deck, while seas washed back and forth across the waist of the ship, crashing through the 'crew strainer' netting at the sides. Everyone on deck wore a harness and clipped on. The helm fought hard to stay upright and hold a course.

We made good speed, driven before the gale, with just two storm sails set. Foam streaked waves rose up behind the poop deck, lifted the ship and tossed her aside. No longer living at an angle, we lurched from hand hold to hand hold. Below, the galley struggled, dishes crashing, Dutch expletives mixed with English. But they coped, and produced a creditable breakfast and lunch for all who could face it.

Through the day the storm steadily abated, but the waves were still large enough to crash over the ship as the Dutch coast hove into view. Soon afterwards we could see the entrance to IJmuiden harbour, our access route to Amsterdam. Still under sail, the captain now at the helm, we squeezed into the harbour mouth, felt the swell subside, and hurried to our stations to hand the sails so we could make our way through the locks. While we waited clearance from the authorities, we toasted our safe return, then partied late into the night.

In a way not foreseen by my earlier calculations, it truly had been the longest day.

The following morning, with no further worries of whether or not I was cheating, Mary and I boarded our plane for home. I was delighted to have accomplished the tick on the Greenwich Light Vessel box of my quest.

---

[1] www.barkeuropa.com.

[2] James Cook, *A Voyage Towards the South Pole and Round the World*, Volume 2, Entry for 21st June 1775. Available at www.gutenberg.net.

[3] Charles Darwin, *The Voyage of the Beagle*, entry for 19th August1836. Available at www. gutenburg.net.

[4] James Cook, *A Voyage Towards the South Pole and Round the World*, Volume 1, entry for 6th March 1774, available at www.gutenburg.net.

# Jersey

49° 13′ N        2° 12′ W

South 4, 19 miles, Fair, 1015, Rising slowly

July 2007

Returning from my *Europa* voyage, and another near miss with Sandettie, I judged the time was right to try another, nearer to home, coastal station. Jersey would be ideal. It is well served with ferries and the train journey to the ports could not be too difficult. But being summer, there are always so many calls on our time that it was with difficulty that we found a couple of days to travel. An additional difficulty became apparent as I tried to piece together the schedule: it was clear that ferry timings are usually calculated for motorists, not for train travellers.

However, we had a secret weapon, recently acquired folding bikes! After some disastrous travels with bikes when our bookings had been dishonoured and when we had found no space on trains, we decided to pre-empt the problem. Folding bikes also give access to the Underground and to buses if necessary. As I attempted to schedule the remaining coastal stations, it became clear that personal transport would be necessary, and that trains and ferries would not provide all the public transport needed. So bikes it would be, and folders were therefore a useful option.

Some research on the web, and through cycle magazines, revealed a surprising variety of styles, capabilities and prices. We had almost decided on a quite expensive model when a visit to our local bike shop turned up an even better option, at about half the price. We needed a capability for some off-road travel, but definitely not 'mud bashing'. Local cycle routes gave us the necessary confidence that we could get along well with our new acquisitions, so we were prepared for the challenge ahead.

Researching the Jersey weather station on the web showed that the Jersey Met Office is quite distinct from the UK Met Office, though like all meteorologists they work closely together and share data openly. Their web site was helpful, giving contact details and a location, at Jersey Airport. So it was that I decided to have a quick look on Google Earth before we departed. I had a list which I thought gave longitude and latitude for each of the coastal stations. A location was given for the Jersey station, so in anticipation of finding the airport, I zoomed in on that position, only to see, well the sea! It appeared to be off the south-west tip of Jersey. Further zooming showed the presence of a lighthouse, which my map confirmed as La Corbiere. Had this been the original location?

An email to Jersey Met Office provided a swift and helpful reply. No, the observation point had been at the Airport for many years, at least twenty which is as far back as anyone could remember. It had moved within the vicinity of the airport, but not far. No explanation was available for the location given, La Corbiere is unmanned, and did not have weather recording equipment. They should be in a position to know! Nearby there used to be a coastguard station, so it is possible that was the observation station in the distant past. Meantime, in preparation for our impending departure, we found a BBC website which reported the longitude and latitude of my chosen observation stations, and a host more besides. Wherever I had obtained my first list, it clearly did not give the information that I thought it gave.

Weather recording in Jersey started in 1894 when the Jesuit priest Father Marc Dechevrens arrived and started keeping detailed records of his observations made at the Jesuit house, Maison St. Louis in St. Helier. Previously he had made weather observations while stationed in China. By the time an official Met service was established in the early 1950s, some 60 years of records were in existence, though with some gaps as priests came and went. But by the mid 1920s, a strong tradition of weather observation was established, and another Jesuit, Father Rey, built instruments himself to improve accuracy. This proved a useful skill during the war, when Jersey was occupied by the Nazis, and the good priest could put his skill to use building radios. By the early 1970s, Father Rey was the sole remaining Jesuit on the island, but continued his observations well into old age, stopping only when he broke a leg and had to retire to France. The Jersey Met Office web site[1] gives a full account, and deserved praise for this pioneering effort.

Getting to Poole by train necessitates two changes for us, at Guildford and Woking. Our schedule gave plenty of time for each change, anticipating the odd platform change, perhaps steps to negotiate and maybe even the need to actually fold the bikes. But perhaps we should have just left a little more time for the all too easily anticipated train delays. At Guildford, there was much confusion about the train time, due to 'defective points' somewhere, so when our train did arrive, it was very overcrowded. However, forewarned by a helpful station attendant we knew where the bike loading place would be, and with a little pushing and squeezing we boarded. The bike spaces were hogged by a passenger with bulky baggage, but with a little insistence, and some bad grace, she moved and we stowed the unfolded bikes. Just one stop took us to Woking and an easy cross-platform change. To avoid a repeat, we decided to fold the bikes this time, but clearly we had not rehearsed this well enough, as they appeared impossible to fit in the bags. So when the train arrived, we boarded with half packed bikes, but in contrast this train was almost empty, so stowing was no problem.   We could enjoy a quiet lunch, sandwiches made before we left home.

Arrival at Poole was no problem, nor was unfolding the bikes and finding the route to the town centre, and onwards to the ferry. Being now somewhat early, we checked out the route to the boarding point, and were a little dismayed to find it took us across a narrow swing bridge, shared with buses, port traffic and the usual impatient drivers.   Not being willing to die for our road rights, we dismounted and walked across the parallel footbridge.

Our new folding bikes were attracting quite a bit of attention and admiring glances.   Other cyclists waiting with us to board the Condor Ferries Catamaran were very curious and even envious of our new acquisitions.   Maybe we should have sought sponsorship from the supplier, but it was too late for that now.

Once aboard, and out to sea, the somewhat indifferent weather cleared, and we sat on deck in warm afternoon sunshine for the whole journey.   First stop was St Peter Port in Guernsey, looking much more summery than on my previous visit, fresh from my first coastal station, the Channel Light Vessel.   Cars and passengers unloaded and reloaded rapidly before the ferry left again for Jersey.

By the time we docked in St. Helier, the British weather had sprung one of its summer surprises.   In torrential rain we disembarked, and sheltered, ironically, in a car park before sloshing our way through puddles to our digs at Havre des Pas, just around the headland from the harbour.   We knocked several times, but no reply.   Since it was now quite late, we began to worry if our hosts had given up on us and gone out.   But a phone call led to the door being reluctantly opened, and with some bad grace we were shown to a rather shabby room.   Not that anything was dirty, or worn out, rather everything looked so out of date as to be almost retro, but lacking the retro attraction.   Given the cost of any accommodation on Jersey, I would have expected something a bit more imaginative. With our bikes stowed in the back garden, we found a nearby restaurant serving Portuguese food and had an amusing but adequate meal before retiring for the night.

In the morning, our bad feelings about the accommodation multiplied. The basement breakfast room was stuffed with too big, too heavy chairs (clearly bought as a cheap job lot) and flimsy tables on which were set out bowls already filled with cornflakes. My protest about an expected choice of cereals was dealt with offhandedly, and I was waved to a sideboard. Clearly I was now labelled as a troublemaker. Did we dare do the tea or coffee game? No, I opted for tea, but Ginny was happy enough with the pot of instant coffee that arrived.

But enough of quibbles. The sun was out again, and in the bay outside the hotel was a glory of early seaside holidays, a large seawater swimming pool, Havre des Pas bathing pool. Quite a sight, a splendid piece of Victorian architecture, a tidal swimming pool with a wide sunbathing terrace originally opened in 1895. It has changing facilities, showers and a cafe, and is home to a sea-swimming club. After falling into disrepair in the 1980s, a major re-fit took place in 2001 and it is now open (to the very hardy) year round. In the summer, it has lifeguards on duty, but is free to all comers. It is so built as to be flooded twice a day by the tide, and between the tides provides a platform for the beautiful people to sun themselves, should the sun oblige. But we had little enough time to explore, we were anxious to be away, quit our unsatisfactory accommodation and to be off to explore the island and its weather station.

Our first port of call was going to be Maison St. Louis. When it operated as a Jesuit seminary it must have been beautifully placed on a hill overlooking St. Helier. But now it's surrounded by urban sprawl, houses for the tax exiles and their banking chums. We found the house itself and its entrance easily enough. It was beautifully maintained but it appeared deserted. We walked around the gardens and found the weather recording instruments laid out on the lawn.  Through the windows we could see that the building was far from unused, but there was nobody about to ask.

Setting off again, we followed the narrow roads leading to the airport.  Jersey prides itself on being cycle friendly, but with narrow roads and high hedges it's not always the most comfortable place to cycle.  However, drivers do tend to be rather courteous and mostly cautious, so we reached the airport terminal without too much concern.  Though I had had an email correspondence with John at the Jersey Met office, I had not told him that we would be visiting nor asked if we could see his office and the weather recording equipment.  Looking around the terminal building it was not obvious where the Met office would be situated.  So I went to the information desk, introduced myself and asked if we could visit John in the Met office.  In my cycle gear, I must have looked suspicious because the man behind the desk asked me a number of questions before telephoning John to ask if it was all right to give me the directions to his office.  Luckily he recalled our email exchanges and was happy to see us.  His office turned out to be in the original terminal building, now used largely for administration as a new terminal building provides the necessary services for passengers.  Entering the aging glass and steel doors was like taking a step back into the 1950s.  But we quickly found what we were looking for and knocked on the door.

John welcomed us into an office environment that was now becoming more familiar.  We could see banks of screens spread about, and one or two staff busily tending to instruments.  We discussed again the location of the observation equipment, and John took us out onto the balcony to show us where it was located, on the far side of the runway.  All the observation data was fed remotely to his office.  I mentioned our earlier visit to Maison St. Louis, and John said that he thought he had seen us on the CCTV. He then went to one of the computers and called up an image from the camera mounted on top of Maison St. Louis.  First he directed the camera at the instruments in the garden where we had been earlier in the morning.  Then, with a few mouse clicks, he pointed it to what he referred to as the signal station above the harbour. Much to my surprise, there was a flagstaff displaying Fitzroy's warning for the gale coming from the South. I expressed my surprise that these signals were still hoisted. He said they were hoisted as a matter of tradition, rather than as operational signals. Sometimes they were not hoisted correctly, and looking at the signal now he pointed out that it should have been removed some hours ago. He then showed me how I could find the CCTV cameras on my home computer, and see various places around the town. I did this several times on my return, but about six months later I noticed that the camera screens were clouded with dirty marks, which caused the camera to focus on the screen not on the distant object. Despite several emails, this fault was not fixed so I can no longer look at the signal station. Later attempts to find out more information about the signal station indicated that it had been discontinued and sold sometime around 2005. I think those were probably the last of Fitzroy's gale signals to be displayed anywhere, but I have not been able to confirm this.

We wondered how John had come to be a weather officer working in Jersey. As you can imagine, his was a career with many twists and turns. He asked about my quest, and what trips I had made to other coastal stations. I explained about reaching the Greenwich Light on *Europa* and the Channel Light Vessel on my first expedition, en route for Guernsey. As it happens, he too had made a similar voyage, but rowing from Torquay to Jersey. His exploit rather put mine in the shade, but he was generous in his acknowledgement of my achievements. He did become rather more interested when we discussed my trip to the Greenwich lightship. He had sailed in many parts of the world, but not aboard a tallship, so he asked for the web address of *Europa*. We talked of other adventures, and proposed adventures, and I asked if he had any ideas as to how I might reach Sandettie, was he perhaps planning a rowing trip across the Dover Straits? But he had no suggestion to offer.

We left John preparing the midday GMT weather bulletin and set off ourselves for a closer look at the weather observatory on the far side of the runway.  As you might expect, the weather instruments are in a fenced enclosure, and not accessible to members of the public.  But we took the opportunity to confirm with our pocket GPS that it was indeed the location that we read from the BBC website.

Later we found a sunny spot by the beach to have our lunch, and then continued to have a look at La Corbiere Lighthouse.  This marks the southwestern corner of Jersey, a dangerous coastline with many rocks and reefs to trap the unwary seafarer.  Building it must have been quite a challenge, for it sits atop some difficult rocks which can only be reached by a causeway at low tide.  Fortunately the tide was out as we arrived and we had no trouble making the short journey across the causeway to the gates.  A plaque at the entrance to the lighthouse gives a completion date of 1874, and claims for it a notable first, the first such structure in the world to be built entirely from concrete, rather than traditional stone block work.  The many lighthouses which are built from stone use complex arrangements of interlocking blocks to prevent the sea from eroding and finally demolishing them.  A concrete lighthouse has no chinks and fissures for the sea to probe, so it has stood for the past 130 years without apparent difficulty.  The plaque credits a marine architect, Sir John Coode, with the design assisted by a structural engineer, Imre Bell.  With a total elevation above the sea of 135 feet and a tower height of 62 feet, La Corbière is not among the giants of the lighthouse world, but has quietly and reliably fulfilled its duty all these years.

So now we were fully satisfied with our visit, and found that cycle-friendly Jersey had indeed built some dedicated cycle facilities.  At one time a narrow gauge railway ran along the coast, west from St Helier, and the bed of this railway has now been converted, as have so many other deserted railways, to serve as a cycle track, leading directly to the centre of St Helier.  With a favourable breeze behind us, and the traffic free route, we had plenty of time to enjoy a cream tea along the way. But before long it was time to be heading back to the port for our journey home.

This time, our crossing of the channel would be on a conventional ferryboat, not a catamaran. Its departure was scheduled for around nine o'clock in the evening, so we sought out a meal in the town before we left. On board the ferry, we stowed our bicycles and found our cabin, comfortable, well appointed, with its own facilities. The owners of our B&B would do well to copy this example, and see what is available in relation to the cost. We made our way to the bar, and sat on deck with a glass of wine, watching the western sky glow with the setting sun. As the ferry pulled out of harbour, we could see the characteristic flashing, 5 seconds lit followed by 5 seconds dark, from our now familiar lighthouse at La Corbiere.

In the morning, we were glad of our bikes to make our way from the port through Portsmouth, still sleeping on a Saturday morning, to the train station for the last step of our journey home. Another weather station was now more than just a name and a dot on the map.

---

[1] www.jerseymet.com for more details.

# Valentia

51° 56′ N          10° 14′ W

East southeast 5, 25 miles, Fair, 1009, Rising

April 2008

In the depths of winter, thoughts of Coastal Stations bubbled under the surface. Once I have an idea in my mind, it's difficult to shift it. But while my schedule in the winter is not so busy, travel is not so attractive. And I was not making much progress on my list. Now in theory, Valentia should be an easy visit for me. I come from Ireland and returned regularly to see my elderly mother who, well into her nineties, had finally agreed to move to a care home. But these were flying visits, quite literally. And that broke the rules I had set myself. So, if I was to achieve my aim, I would have to make a particular effort.

There had been an opportunity to make the visit in a rather stylish way and I had been tempted to push for it. Delighted by my sighting of the Greenwich Light Vessel from the tallship *Europa* earlier in the year, I imagined that I could repeat the experience, this time visiting Valentia from another tallship, *Asgard II*, the Irish national sail training ship. I had sailed aboard her as a volunteer on a number of occasions and so I was to sail again, this time joining in Galway and leaving in Cork. Coming winter or not, this might provide the opportunity I was looking for. There was the plane journey, which could be avoided with some difficulty. But was it worth the gamble? Particularly since there was no guarantee that we would pass anywhere near the island, let alone see the weather station itself. I pondered the idea of bribing the Captain to put in at the little harbour, Knightstown, on the island. But it did not work out that way.

I joined *Asgard II* as planned in Galway. Nearby her mooring in the tidal basin, a monument, donated by the City of Genoa, records the part played by Galway in the career of none other than Christopher Columbus. As a sea captain in command of a Genoese trading ship, he visited Galway, reportedly in 1477. There it is believed that he found evidence, carried by the Gulf Stream, that there was land beyond the horizon. Depending on the season, all manner of vegetation is washed up on the shores of the west of Ireland. The types of vegetation shown to Columbus were unknown in Europe, so he concluded they must come from Asia, and the Atlantic promised a short cut, westwards, to the fabulous riches of the east. He may have got all kinds of things about his proposed voyage wrong, but he got one major thing right. He had worked out that in the north Atlantic, the prevailing winds blow from the southwest, while further south, along the coast of Morocco, the prevailing winds blow from the northeast. This was the key to a successful round trip out into the Atlantic, and, as he fondly hoped, to a new trade route to Japan and the East. But this insight into the key feature of what determines the weather of our islands was not used systematically in connection with weather reporting until several hundred years later.

We sailed down the west coast of Ireland, unseasonably good weather easing our passage, and providing brilliant views of the spectacular scenery. At night, in a moonless sky, dolphins played under the bow, streaking through the remains of the autumnal bio-luminescence bloom. And Valentia Island came into view in the early morning light, spectacular in its way, but offering no sign of its weather station. The Captain remained unswayed by my suggestions of a visit. He was all too well aware of the Atlantic gales coming, preferring to round the treacherous south west coast of Ireland while the good sailing weather held. Rather tragically, this was to be my last voyage aboard *Asgard II*. In the early hours of a September morning the following year in the Bay of Biscay, the ship started taking on water and sank some hours later. Thankfully there were no casualties, but I felt as if I had lost an old and very dear friend.

In fact, Valentia weather station is no longer located on the island. It was moved to the mainland many years ago now, keeping the name for its historic connections as it was one of Fitzroy's original weather stations, first established in 1860. Valentia was the terminal of the first trans-Atlantic telegraph cables, and so from there a well-established telegraph connection existed to London, ideal for his purposes. Not only was it located in the direct path of the prevailing weather systems from the southwest that so determine the weather in the rest of the United Kingdom, but its direct telegraph connection to London provided up to 24 hours' notice of the arrival of weather fronts and gales. The telegraph station itself was staffed by any number of reliable operators who would make the necessary observations and transmit them as necessary. Later, a purpose built observatory was constructed and staffed by the Met Office itself.

The observatory was transferred to the mainland, just outside Cahirciveen in County Kerry, within view of the island, in 1892. This was deemed necessary partly because Valentia Island itself was not always easy to reach, and telegraphy had improved to the point that the trans-Atlantic connection was no longer relevant. Many years later the island was connected to the mainland with a causeway and bridge, but the observatory was by then too well established to consider a move. Valentia weather station was originally established before Ireland's independence in 1922. It was eventually transferred to the newly established Irish Meteorological Service, Met Eireann. Like Malin Head, and a dozen other Irish meteorological stations, weather data from Valentia is freely shared with other meteorological services around Europe and the world.

So it was back to the planning, for a spring visit. A combination of coach, ferry and train would meet the required transport constraints. But the last leg would require either a short cycle journey, or a taxi. I was not completely sure that either bike hire or taxis would be available to coincide with my planned visit, but in Ireland there's always a way to get things done, given time. The Irish Sea is well served by ferry routes, and the Irish national coach operator, Bus Eireann, was offering fantastic fares for a fully inclusive return journey from London to Dublin, just £25! I looked for a suitable opportunity.

I also looked for a suitable travelling companion. Coach and ferry travel in the early spring is not to everyone's taste. But I thought I could tempt a long-standing friend to join in on this almost madcap adventure. After all, it sounded like a challenge and my friend Paul from Somerset was looking for a new challenge. We had known each other since we worked together teaching in Zambia in the early 1970s. His daughters were almost the same age as mine, and they had all begun their own families around the same time, so we were both relatively new grandparents, struggling to come to terms with impending great age and decrepitude. We had also travelled together in the past, not only on bird-watching trips in Africa, but also to Ireland some years previously. The combination of Irish wit, drink and culture, the 'craic' as it is now universally known, proved to be completely compatible with Paul's own tastes. I scarcely had time to sketch the idea before he had agreed to accompany me. He was delighted as I filled in the details, but at the mention of a bike he almost choked. A bike to Paul is a shiny black and chrome machine emitting an ear splitting racket as it disappears in a cloud of dust down the road. He was dubious in the extreme about a machine propelled by his own efforts, an ordinary bicycle. Hopefully, he suggested that we might find a couple of horses or, at the very least, donkeys to take us the last few miles. I could only promise to investigate the possibilities.

Thus it was that in early April I awoke with the Shipping Forecast and Reports from Coastal Stations once again in my ear. I listened attentively for Irish Sea, wind force 2-3 (ideal for a ferry crossing) maybe 6/7 later. 'Later' is a technical term used in this context, meaning in the second half of the reporting period, so in this case hopefully the force 6 or 7 winds (not ideal for a ferry crossing!) would be in the evening, well after we expected to arrive in Ireland. The weather from Valentia sounded interesting: wind from the south west, force 5, recent light rain, visibility 15 miles, pressure 1008 and rising slowly. Not bad for the time of year, though experience told me that this could change very rapidly on that exposed corner of Ireland, jutting out into the Atlantic.

The morning was dull but dry as I took a very early train to Victoria along with some dozen dozing commuters, then walked the few hundred metres to Victoria Coach Station, arriving very early for my coach. It's a long time since I was last in Victoria Coach Station but my memory of it was not mistaken. Great journeys do not begin here. It's not accidental that no one has written '100 Great Coach Journeys to do Before You Die!' and I will not be attempting to. It seems that in the UK, like the US, coach travel is more and more the preserve of the poor. Perhaps it's a class attitude, but I determined that next time I travelled to a distant weather station I would take the train, possibly first class! And I consoled myself with the thought that Gatwick is not much better, but does have vastly more people to cope with. However, it also has vastly better toilets.

There were few takers for the Dublin coach, but ahead of me in the small queue was a pair of souls looking distinctly lost. He clutched a white stick in one hand and her arm with the other. The check-in attendant asked for documents and she shuffled her papers with the attention of one who cannot read, eventually giving the packet to the not-too-happy attendant. My heart sank for them. Later, as we awaited the boarding call, she checked with me my own travel plans and the status of the coach departure. I recognised her accent as that of an Irish traveller, gypsy, as we used to say. We swapped stories, though I was reluctant to share the real purpose of my travels. Instead, I mentioned a visit to my mother, which was true, but only part of the story. It seemed he had lost his sight in a car crash, following a drinking session, which he blamed on former drinking partners spiking his drink. Whatever the truth, the effects were all too evident. Their purpose in travelling to Dublin was to attend a family wedding, though they were not too sure of where to find the family. Travellers in Dublin have just as much trouble finding suitable sites as they do in the UK, and the family could well have been moved on since they were last heard of at the top of O'Connell Street.

Boarding the coach at last, I was relieved that my fellow travellers were as careful of their privacy as I was of mine. They headed for the rear of the bus, while I wanted the view from the front. Now things improved, as the weather cleared and the morning brightened. We passed the Irish Embassy in Grosvenor Square, and were soon speeding up the M1 towards our first stop at the edge of Milton Keynes. There we were joined by two more passengers, a quietly spoken middle-aged Asian couple. Perhaps they didn't like air travel, or were on their own quest. We smiled at each other but kept our distance.

At each stop, where we paused long enough for coffee and a much needed trip to the loo, the drivers and my traveller companions made a swift exit in order to catch a quick cigarette before the journey resumed. Though the coach was equipped with a toilet, the bouncing and shaking made using it nearly as daunting as using one aboard a sailing ship.

At Birmingham, I noticed Paul beaming as we pulled into the coach station and he took the seat beside me. His train journey from Taunton had been uneventful, though busy. I showed him a text message he had sent me in error, obviously intended for a lady in whom he feigned disinterest. 'Could I be missing you already? After only an hour?' The text seemed to show more interest than he was willing to admit, but we both laughed at the vagaries of mobile (mis)communications. Actually we laughed a great deal over our few days' journey, mainly at ourselves, and the many mistakes we had made in the years we had known each other. Paul thinks of himself as stuck in a rut, and part of the reason for the journey for him was to look for possible new directions. But since he has been seeking a new direction for at least ten years, neither of us was very optimistic that the journey would prove the catalyst. However, the search proved endlessly amusing for both of us, and perhaps that was enough.

Paul is also a self confessed Luddite. In Zambia we had both been teachers, but, on leaving, our careers had taken very different paths. I joined the Railways as a researcher in a high tech establishment before moving on to various assignments where computer systems played a leading role. He continued teaching biology for a time, then established an organic smallholding before tiring of the full-time commitment to both school and agriculture. He re-invented himself as a gardener and a writer on organic gardening, specialising in low maintenance garden design and planting. All of which is delightfully low tech. But he had at last come to depend on a mobile phone, and text messaging to keep in touch. As we chewed over his professed Luddism, he was embarrassed to admit that he had just taken delivery of his first ever computer! Under the tutelage of his son-in-law, he was about to take a giant leap for a Luddite and connect to the 'Interweb' as he called it. This was prompted, he claimed, by the recent demise of his beloved typewriter, and the demands of his publisher for electronic copy. So new directions were opening up anyway. This seemed a very good start to his quest.

It seemed no time at all, but a million laughs later, that we arrived in Dun Laoghaire, the port for Dublin and set out into the evening rush hour traffic of Dublin's frenetic development. Crawling through the jams, we were amused by a coach load of young women in front, apparently headed for Northern Ireland, who simulated sex between stuffed toys for our benefit, collapsing with laughter as they did so. How Dublin has changed from the dour days of my childhood there. It has changed in other ways too. At the entrance to the city from the (new) toll bridge, a giant portrait of the Queen stared down on the citizens of the Republic. Above it was the enigmatic title, 'Coming Soon'. I never did work out what it was all about.

Our first stop on arriving in Dublin was to get ourselves established in our chosen hotel, in Malahide, north Dublin, near where my mother is in care. When Paul visited Dublin with me some years ago, we had both stayed with my parents, then younger and in their own house. His visit was remembered with affection by my mother, and with a great deal of humour by both of us. So, after a good meal and a good night's sleep, we collected Mother for a day out, visiting some of her favourite haunts, while taking the opportunity ourselves for some fun.

Paul is a very able bird-watcher. As a child I was interested in birds, but would not have thought of myself as any kind of authority. During the time Paul and I spent together in Zambia, he introduced me to a great variety of African birds, in the process ranging far and wide over the bush and mountains that surrounded us. From him I learned not just the names of birds, but also something of their habits and characteristics. Though he would probably deny it, to me he is definitely a bird expert. So it was something of a surprise when we stepped out of the hotel and, binoculars in hand, Paul froze, pointed and said "What's that?" The object of his interest was a Hooded Crow, common in Ireland, and a bird I well remember from my childhood. It seems that my expert friend had not seen one before, though he had heard of them. A new bird, not often does that happen to an experienced birdman. But later in the day, as we walked along the pier at nearby Howth, the same thing happened again. Again, binoculars snapped to eyes, and there was a Black Guillemot, another first for Paul. Two in a day! Ireland is clearly quite a treasure for bird-watchers.

Later, another Irish treasure provided us with a splendid evening
out. The Abbey Theatre is not just a national institution, but is
famous throughout the world as the home of a host of Irish
playwrights. On Paul's earlier visit, we had seen a stage adaptation
of Flann O'Brian's 'At Swim Two Birds'. Its madcap Irish humour
had us both rocking with laughter, and its catch phrase 'A Pint of
Plain is Your Only Man' had entered a common vocabulary, as a
response to any setback.

On this occasion though it was not Irish humour, but a classic of
ancient Greece that drew us to the Abbey. 'The Burial at Thebes' is
a play by Irish Nobel laureate Seamus Heaney, based on the fifth
century BC tragedy 'Antigone' by Sophocles. The title of the play
recalls Antigone's punishment - to be walled up in a cave - for her
crime, performing a forbidden burial ritual for her disgraced
brother. Her two brothers have killed each other fighting on
different sides of a civil war. Creon, the new king of Thebes, buries
one of the brothers, but refuses burial to the other, who fought on
the losing side. Strange how the deep sentiments of humanity
speak so forcefully across the millennia. We are still horrified by
corpses disrespected, and are often told how enemy soldiers are
buried 'with full military honours'. The beauty of Heaney's poetic
dialogue shines through the horror of the unfolding tragedy, a light
that darkens the despair of dishonour.

After Dublin, the real focus of our travels reasserted itself, getting
to Valentia. Before the financial bubble burst, Ireland's newfound
wealth was being spent in the public as well as the private sector,
and public transport had a good share of investment. So the train
service was now good and busy. Turning up to join the 10:30 train
to Cork, with connecting service to Killarney, we first collected our
tickets and then looked for our train. But Ireland has its own ways,
and its own charm, not lightly replaced by modernity. As a
resident of Dublin, what I used to find exasperating, I now find
warmly amusing. Of course the train was late, but no one seemed
stressed by it, nor particularly concerned about the connecting

service. Looking for our seats, when the train did pull in, we asked assistance from one of the train staff. "Ah, sure the train's not busy, sit wherever you like" was the reassurance we received, and so we did.

It is little known outside Ireland, but the Irish railways were constructed with a different gauge from the standard adopted in Britain and much of the rest of the world. For whatever reason, the engineers laying out Ireland's railroads chose 5ft. 3in. as a suitable gauge. I suppose this didn't matter a great deal in the Victorian age, when almost all railway vehicles were constructed locally. Now however, high tech railways require high tech trains, and building these requires capital investment beyond what would be justified by the needs of a small country alone. So Ireland's new trains are imported, and adapted for the Irish track gauge. Probably most visitors are unaware of this, though I remember being taught about these differences in primary school. Later, when I first went to work in England, I joined the research and development division of what was then British Railways. They say, "Once a railwayman, always a railwayman," so I was delighted to see just how Irish Railways had adapted to international train standards. It's probably sufficient to say "Very well", though the Irish psyche will take longer to adapt. A recent 'scandal' in the newspapers concerned the new tram system in Dublin, where much indignation was aroused when it was 'revealed' in an evening paper that it would use the 'English' track gauge, not the Irish one. Feathers were eventually smoothed when it was pointed out that it was in fact the European gauge, and the trams are not connected to the railway system.

Leaving Dublin's new and rapidly spreading suburbs behind, we were soon in the more traditional Irish countryside, small fields, tall and unkempt hedges and mostly livestock farming. Passing the Curragh, home to Ireland's racehorse industry, the fields gave way to cropped pasture and exercise paddocks, with suitably affluent housing close by. We saw continuous evidence of the upgrading work in progress for the railway, but gratifyingly the distinctive

Irish railway architecture, with stations built from grey granite, seems safe and is being carefully restored where necessary. In contrast to a coach journey, a railway journey gives the satisfactory feeling of being a real journey, of travel as it can and should be. I doubt that Robert Louis Stevenson would have written "to travel hopefully is a better thing than to arrive" if he had been obliged to go by coach.

Maybe the first part of this train trip would not qualify as one of the world's great railway journeys. But once we changed trains at Mallow, and headed west towards Killarney in Kerry, the scenery took a dramatic turn for the better. Ireland's highest mountains, the MacGillycuddy's Reeks, loomed on the horizon, bare and daunting, with a good coating of snow on the tops. I struggled to identify Carrauntoohil, Ireland's highest peak, at 1039 metres. As a youngster, I had climbed it on several occasions, an exhilarating experience, perhaps to be repeated in the future.

At last we arrived at Killarney's very traditional station, and emerged to this most traditional of Irish towns, with its characteristic horse-drawn buggies, known locally as Jaunting Cars. Paul's eyes widened as he contemplated trying to persuade one of the drivers to rent him the horse for an evening hack along the edges of Killarney's world famous lakes. But by the time we had checked into our hotel, the Jaunting Cars were nowhere to be seen, so we settled for an early evening stroll along the still wintry lakes. With the snowcapped MacGillycuddy's Reeks as a dramatic backdrop, and evening sunlight streaming through the bare trees, it was easy to see how Bing Crosby, amongst others, got carried away with the beauty of the place.

Ireland's tourist industry may play a bit on the 'Quaint Auld Ireland' theme, but at its best, if it's well done, the result is indeed quaint and charming. We wanted two more things to add to the beauty of Killarney, a proper Irish stew and some traditional Irish music. Our friendly hotel staff were more than happy to oblige with suggestions, and about half an hour later we sat down to a really good Irish meal, Spinach Cream Soup with Guinness and Treacle Bread, followed by Irish Stew, washed down with, what else, a couple of pints of 'plain'! Irish stew was a great favourite of my mother's, and a fond memory from my childhood. It is much copied, and miscopied, in Ireland and abroad. I have had pale imitations in eating houses far and near, cheap and expensive, so I believe I am well equipped to judge a decent Irish Stew. This was a decent Irish Stew! For the uninitiated, here are some guidelines: the potatoes should be cooked in the stew, the gravy should look thin, but taste strong, there should be bones within the meat, and the only seasonings should be salt, pepper and fresh parsley. Root vegetables, carrots, turnips or parsnips, complete the full picture.

Thus fortified, we went in search of the music. Now in Killarney, any music will to some extent be targeted at the tourist trade (us!), but, as with Irish stew, it can be well done or a poor pastiche of itself. Again we were lucky, or well guided, or both. We arrived at the Killarney Grand, a busy but not too crowded pub with a blazing fire and a pair of musicians just about to strike up. A kindly gentleman made space for us at his table near the players, but refused our offer of a drink. So we settled down as the young dark-haired lady fiddler tuned up with her accomplice. He was a huge man, with a huge shaggy beard under a seafarer's cap perched on a huge head of shaggy hair. His huge hands gripped a suitably large instrument which neither of us recognised, but he certainly looked the part of the travelling musician. Without any written music, the pair played jigs and reels to the satisfaction of all around, ourselves and our companion at the table included.

When the musicians took a break, Paul, himself a guitar player, went to talk to the huge man and I struck up a conversation with the gentleman who had refused a drink. It turned out he was a 'pioneer', a non-drinker since childhood, and showed me his mug of tea, though he didn't want that refilled either. But he was born, and still lived, locally, and came to the Killarney Grand most nights for the music. Like many an Irishman his age, he was a retired civil servant who had never married, but stayed at home while his brothers and sisters left for Dublin or abroad. Now he was alone at home, and came out to enjoy the company. As a local, with a wealth of choice of musical pubs, his regular choice must be something of an accolade. At least we thought so.

Paul returned with the news that the mystery instrument was a type of bouzouki! This is not by any means a traditional Irish pub instrument, but it blended well with the fiddle to give a really good sound. Irish music has a long tradition, and until comparatively recently was almost unknown outside Ireland. So when a world audience began to take an interest, it was still relatively 'pure'. But as often happens, exposure to the wider world of music, traditional, jazz and pop, has resulted in some very attractive fusion, a genre exploited to considerable success by The Chieftains. Starting as a very traditional Irish music group in the sixties, they developed a style of their own, and then built co-operative ventures with Van Morrison, Ry Cooder, Marianne Faithful and many others. Mind you, not all 'fusion' works. At eleven o'clock, the traditional music stopped to make way for a 'band', guitar, keyboards and vocals, over-amplified for the space, and certainly not what we had come for. With our retired tea-drinking companion, we made our way out into the cold, and to our respective lodgings.

Morning dawned bright and cold, with a chill wind blowing across the snow-sprinkled peaks. Now we had to contend with another Irish tradition, early breakfast. This, to the Irish tourist trade begins around eight thirty, somewhat late by our expectations, so we opted for an early morning walk, and late breakfast, after nine. Once, in the west of Ireland, a request for 'early breakfast' had been answered with a suggestion that nine or so should be early enough. We still seemed to be the first to arrive. What's that about there being no word in Irish for 'mãnana'? It seems nowhere in Ireland is there the need to express quite that sense of urgency!

The bus for Cahirciveen arrived more or less on time and so we left Killarney on our way further west. The first part of the journey, as far as Killorglin, was unremarkable but soon afterwards the road descended to the seashore and followed the beautiful and wild coast of Dingle Bay. Again we were lucky with the weather which stayed clear as we came in sight of our stop, a B&B appropriately named 'The Final Furlong', where the driver was happy to stop and let us off. With a name like that, there had to be a horsy connection, and again Paul sensed the possibility of riding. But the lady who greeted us at the door quickly explained that the horses were still indoors for the winter, and the stables would not open for a month or so, and then only if the ground dried out sufficiently.

But she was happy to drive us into the town, to the bike rental shop, and I was much relieved. Horse riding is not a skill I wish to acquire. Cahirciveen is not a beautiful town, lacking any real centre. Its buildings are strung out along a single main street for a mile or more. Its most notable building is a large Roman Catholic church, built and named in honour of perhaps the most famous Irish politician, Daniel O'Connell (1775-1847), who came from the town. Known as 'The Liberator', he is best remembered for his work to repeal of the Penal Laws discriminating against Roman Catholics. Dublin's main street was renamed in his honour and his statue looks out from its centre on O'Connell Bridge. Perhaps he is the only Irish politician to have a church named after him. Somehow I cannot imagine a similar honour being awarded to any current politician, Irish or not.

Much to Paul's amusement, we collected the bikes, though he declined the offered helmet, for the final stage of our journey. Despite his protests that he had not ridden a bike for some forty years, we peddled steadily west out of Cahirciveen, and not long afterwards, as we rounded a bend, we were face to face with the long awaited weather station! The building looked new, set just off the road in large grounds sweeping down to the sea. We cycled through the car park, and as we approached the door, a young lady came down the stairs and opened the door as if we were expected.

I stammered something of our intentions, and, again as if expected, she indicated the stairs and reassured us that we would find the meteorologist in the room at the top.

Doffing my cycle helmet, I knocked and a friendly voice bid us enter. The voice belonged to Brian Walsh, the young meteorologist in sole charge of a vast bank of instruments in a well-equipped weather lab. From the windows we could see far and wide, north over the grounds and across Dingle Bay, and west towards Valentia Island itself. Brian welcomed us, but asked us to wait for a minute or two as he was preparing to launch the midday weather balloon. On the desk was a small instrument package in a light plastic shell, and what looked like a giant condom, neatly packed in a sleeve, the

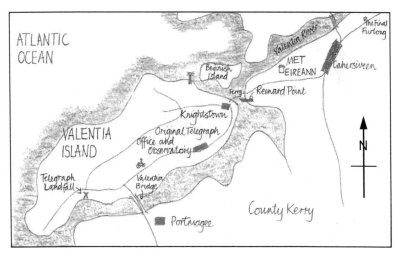

un-inflated balloon. Brian attached the instrument package to the bottom of the balloon and suggested we go outside to the balcony to watch the launch, which would be automatic once he had placed his handiwork in the launcher. How exciting to see a real weather balloon launched!

On the balcony, we were soon joined by Brian, who pointed to the centre of the roof above which what looked like a large dustbin was emerging to our view.  It stopped, and the lid lifted to one side.  Now the balloon itself emerged, slowly at first, much smaller than I imagined, swinging in the breeze and dragging its little instrument package after it.  We watched as it lifted slowly at first, then rose more rapidly into the now hazy sky and was gradually lost from view.  We asked what height it would reach before it inevitably burst and fell to earth again.  Hopefully 33,000 metres, Brian replied.  At first I imagined he had made a mistake, surely it was feet, not metres, or maybe I had misheard.  But no, Brian confirmed, 33,000 metres, about 100,000 feet!  That's twice the height at which Concorde flew.  This upward journey would take some two hours, and during that time the instrument package would relay readings every few seconds.  The readings are displayed in real time on an instrument in the lab, and published graphically on the internet.

Not all weather stations launch weather balloons.  But Valentia launches two different types.  Every twelve hours, a balloon like we had just seen is launched.  The instrument package is not recovered, and Brian seemed unperturbed by two a day falling on the surrounding hills and sea.  What happens to them, I wondered?  Once a week, the station launches an ozone monitoring balloon.  This is altogether a more complex instrument, therefore more costly.  The instrument package offers a reward to the finder who returns it to Met Eireann, but not too many are returned.  Launching it is more complex too, and the automated launcher used for the twice daily balloons cannot be used.  Instead, a couple of staff fill the balloon from helium bottles and release it manually.  In the frequently windy conditions of Ireland's far west coast, this can be quite a challenge.

Back in the lab, Brain checked that the data transmissions were being recorded correctly and then showed us the balloon's upward progress on a graph.  These observations, as with all meteorological observations, are shared freely with the meteorological services throughout the world.   Not all observations are automatic at manned stations. For some observations, the manual instruments are still the instruments of choice. But all observations, manual or automatic, are coded by hand for rapid transmission by email to Met Eireann headquarters in Dublin. From there, they are made available to other forecasters, including, of course, the BBC.

The meteorologist in charge mostly works alone, so Brian was pleased to have some company for a time. Though the building in which he worked was new, he explained that Met Eireann keeps a collection of historical instruments in Westwood House, the old house we could see from the window in the grounds. This is the house to which the weather station was moved from the island itself, and which is now largely a museum. He suggested we visit; that someone there would show us around. He also suggested we have a look around the Phenological Garden on the way to see the museum. Both of us looked up, surprised. What was a Phenological Garden? This was not a word either of us had heard before. My father often said it's a dull day when you don't learn something new. In which case, today was turning out to be a very bright day indeed!

Brian explained the idea behind the garden. It contains a number of 'standard' plants, trees and shrubs whose progress is recorded meticulously over the years. Their progress is measured by the date of such things as the first buds, the first green shoots, the leaves turning colour, flowering, fruit setting and so on. Each event is looked for and monitored closely. Over the years, a pattern can be observed, and not surprisingly, the pattern is for earlier springs. Such gardens exist throughout Europe, sponsored initially by the Humboldt University[1] in Germany. To make the comparisons more meaningful, the original gardens, set up in the early 1950s, were stocked with cuttings from the same plants, genetically identical specimens whose progress would stand comparison. The originators of the idea could have had no idea of just how important these observations would be in our time. Paul was fascinated. As a semi-professional gardener, perhaps he should know more of such gardens, perhaps there was a story here for his other semi-profession, writing about gardening.   We went to inspect.

Perhaps not surprisingly, in early April, on the windy west coast of Ireland, there seemed little sign of spring, despite the brilliant sunshine.   Paul managed to identify some of the specimens, but others were new to him.  Not all had labels, after all this was not set up as a botanical garden, and those who ran it would have no need of labels.   We hoped to find help in the main house itself, and looked for an open entrance.   Inside we found a wonderful collection of instruments, some dating back to the original establishment of the observatory.    Over the years, more sophisticated instruments replaced earlier ones, though even the earliest were still capable of providing very accurate readings. However, modern meteorologists would be unhappy to be surrounded by all that mercury in the older instruments.

Unfortunately, the staff member responsible for the garden was away that day, but her colleagues gave us an email address and assured us that she would be happy to provide further information on her return.   However, after our own return home, we checked for information on Phenological Gardens on the web, and were surprised at just how much data is available.  With relative ease I could check on the movement of significant spring events in my own area over a long period of years.   I am surprised that the source of this information is not more widely quoted.  Whenever I have seen articles or TV programs that mention the effects of climate change on the arrival of spring, the source is generally given as an amateur gardener, or keen observer.  But there are these records, which have been meticulously kept to high standards throughout Europe.  We should hear more of them.

Feeling we had had great value from our visit, we said our goodbyes and mounted up for a visit to the island itself.  It had been great to see the weather station, and to learn of its functioning from Brian, who would now forever be the 'face' of Valentia on future Weather Reports. But somehow we absolutely had to visit the island, to see the original station and the landing place of the first trans-Atlantic telegraph cable, which after all was the reason it was established here in the first place.

A short ride brought us to Renard Point, the mainland terminal for the Valentia Island ferry. This was delightfully relaxed. Though there is a timetable of sorts, in reality at this time of year the little drive-on drive-off ferry goes back and forth whenever there are a couple of customers. Still in bright sunshine, we wobbled down the ramp and up to the little village of Knightstown, now in search of lunch. In the first pub we came to we found the ideal menu, another Irish favourite, boiled bacon and cabbage.

A friendly service was provided by yet another new Irish institution. In a reversal of fortunes from my childhood, Ireland was at that time a country of net immigration, and despite large numbers of arrivals from the new Europe, the main source of migrants was the UK. Our barman was from Birmingham, once home to a large Irish emigrant population. And in truth, many of the arrivals from the UK had some Irish connection, perhaps a spouse, parent or a grandparent. However, that does not mitigate the surprise I felt when greeted in a very cheery English accent by a barman in an Irish pub! We ordered our food, and the inevitable pints of 'plain' and took our seats.

A few minutes later the cook emerged, very apologetic, to explain that the parsley sauce, the traditional accompaniment to boiled bacon and cabbage, was all gone. We had to make do with gravy, no real substitute, to accompany the vast mound of bacon, cabbage and mash.

Thus fortified, we rode on to Telegraph Field, past the rows of cottages built by the cable companies for their employees and the site of the original observatory. In fact, both the observatory and its instruments were located at various places on the island at different times. Above the cliffs at Telegraph Field, stands a memorial stone, appropriately made from Valentia slate. It displays representations of the various types of cable used to land the different trans-Atlantic connections over the years, and records the role played by the telegraph in finally establishing the correct longitude of American observatories in relation to European longitudes. Amazingly, despite the efforts of such magnificent surveyors as Fitzroy himself, by 1866 there was still an uncertainty of some 1000 metres between the measurements on each side of the Atlantic. With the help of the cable, this was corrected, to the relief of mariners everywhere.

The first successful cable was laid by Isambard Kingdom Brunel's famous ship *Great Eastern*, built originally as a passenger ship, but unsuccessful in that role. After Brunel's death, she was converted for use as a cable ship, and laid a number of international telegraph cables. It's difficult to imagine how it would have looked at the time, the largest ship ever built standing just off the cliffs, while the cable was led ashore, then steaming ever so slowly, about walking pace, out over the horizon towards Canada. The laying of the cable is something of an epic story in itself.

From here, almost as far west as it's possible to be in Ireland, our homeward journey began. By now, the famously variable Atlantic weather had begun to vary. The wind freshened, thankfully from behind, and the rain started. We dashed for Knightstown, across the ferry and into the warmth and comfort of a very traditional Cahirciveen pub, with yet another English barman, for a pre-dinner pint. By now it was dark, but we found a restaurant nearby and enjoyed a local fish meal, of a far higher standard, and price, than would have been possible in an earlier time.

Regrettably, there was no music to be had in Cahirciveen that night, so we set about returning to our B&B. By now it was pitch dark with no moon, and the roads were thankfully very quiet, but without any lighting whatsoever, cycling, even finding the road, was a real challenge. Eventually, suspecting we were near the Final Furlong, we waited until a car came by to illuminate the sign sufficiently to read it, and gratefully stumbled our way up the drive.

In the morning we gathered our things together before taking a quick walk in the early morning sun to check on the wildlife on the bay. It all looked very benign now, but I'm sure that when the Atlantic lows move in, it's a very different scene. We cycled back into Cahirciveen to return the bikes, and take the bus back to Killarney.

Ireland has an amazing capacity to surprise visitors, and returning exiles too. While we were having a coffee and waiting for the bus, Paul's jaw dropped in a now characteristic expression of surprise. This time I knew it could not be some ornithological rarity that caught his attention, so turned slowly to check. Outside, soldiers with automatic rifles at the ready patrolled up and down the main street, in poses more reminiscent of Basra or Belfast than a quiet Irish town. Across the street a well armoured Land Rover stood outside the local bank. Nobody else gave the scene a second glance, it was just an ordinary delivery of cash in an area that had seen IRA activity in the past. Later we saw the soldiers buy take-away coffee and buns at another local café, looking more relaxed than I would have imagined possible.

The return journey was much the reverse of the journey out. The main difference was that we travelled back on a night coach. Somehow, the bus company manages to run two services a day from London to Dublin, one in the daytime, the other at night, but only the night-time one back. How is that possible? Are they importing coaches surreptitiously? Or do they have a high accident rate?

So we waited for the boarding call with many more passengers than on the way over. A black lady behind us in the queue had a large amount of badly packed luggage, and from her accent we could tell she came from southern Africa. This she confirmed, but she was from Mozambique, not South Africa as we imagined. She had come to Ireland looking for work, as so many do, but as she said "she had not been lucky" so was going to Paris where she had a daughter studying. We helped her load her luggage and wished her luck in France.

The ferry we joined this time left from the centre of Dublin, so we were soon aboard and settled in the bar (where else?) as we sailed down the Liffey towards the open sea, past the colourful lights of the port area. Dublin has been a port since at least Viking times, but has always had a problem with silting up. A scheme to prevent this was devised in the late 18th century by none other than William Bligh, the famous captain of the *Bounty*. He studied the tidal streams in the bay, and came up with a design involving the construction of a long wall, or bull, out into Dublin Bay. When it was finished, the port became largely self dredging. The silt that had clogged the port now built up on the outside of the wall, and created a huge sand island, called the Bull Island. This has long been a nature reserve, of particular importance to migrating birds, and a bird-watchers' haven in the heart of Dublin Bay.

So, we were soon enough back in Holyhead, and back on the coach to doze away the midnight miles until we parted in the pre-dawn of Birmingham coach station. We both felt the journey had been hugely rewarding, in objectives achieved, and in terms of new challenges to explore. Valentia must be the most westerly Phenological Garden in Europe, but where are the others? Which is the most northerly? The most easterly? Southerly? A whole host of new challenges awaits, thankfully the list of things to do never gets shorter!

---

[1] www.agrar.hu-berlin.de/struktur/institute/nptw/agrarmet/phaenologie/ipg

# Ronaldsway

54° 5' N          4° 38' W

North northwest 3, 25 miles, Fair, 1010, Rising

April 2009

Not for the first time during this quest have I been amazed at the time that elapsed since my previous venture.  No amount of planning seems to make achieving the actual visits easier.  There are always simply too many good things to do.  However, I blocked out 10 days in my diary, determined to visit the Isle of Man and Malin Head on a single journey.  Then I began looking for a travelling companion.  My buddy Paul from my previous Irish escapade sounded excited at first, but then affirmed that as a paid up biker he could not consider visiting the Isle of Man outside the TT Race season.  And I would not consider a visit during the races.  My lady wife, Ginny, was in the early stages of recovery from a foot operation and so she was not available.  On the spur of the moment, having bumped into each other in Waitrose, I suggested to another friend, Andy, that he might like an adventure.  His interest increased as I outlined my suggestions, and we agreed to discuss the matter further over a few pints later in the week.

The Ronaldsway coastal station is at the airport.  Its name conjures up images of childhood holidays for me.  In fact, it was the first place I ever travelled to on a plane. When I was about the age of six, my parents took my brother and myself to the Isle of Man for a summer holiday, and much to my childhood horror, we flew. I don't remember, but apparently I worried for days about the aeroplane crashing. What I do remember is going to Dublin Airport in my Grandfather's car, and there being loads of space to run around in the terminal building. Then we were led out to the plane, a DC3 Dakota. We boarded at the back, up a few steps, and then climbed up the aisle to our seats, as the plane sat on the tarmac tail down. My fear must have given way to excitement, for that's the emotion I most strongly recollect as we raced down the runway. The tail rose, and the plane seemed to leap into the air. I do remember lots of things about the flight; looking out at the ground rushing by, then falling away; seeing the houses becoming smaller and smaller; the sea and seemingly tiny ships, all magic to my childish eye. Those were the days when a photographer awaited the arrival of visitors on a plane, and took pictures as each group descended the steps. With only about 25 passengers, these things were possible, and expected.

It seems to me that I always knew the airport we were heading for was called Ronaldsway. Perhaps there was something about the name that just stuck in my mind, from childhood. Certainly, I remember other visits there too, on other childhood holidays, but just why the name stuck, I cannot say. After my early holidays I didn't go to the Isle of Man again until 1999, when I joined what would be the first of many tallship voyages, this one aboard the Sail Training Association's schooner *Sir Winston Churchill*. We started from Liverpool, but as luck would have it, when we arrived in Douglas it was my turn to stand watch for the central four hours of our stay, so I had no time to explore much beyond Douglas itself. But I did accompany a fellow sailor to the railway station and was delighted to find that the little steam trains that I remembered from my childhood visits were still very much in operation, much loved and beautifully restored. Later, researching my visit to the coastal station, I was overjoyed to find a railway station at Ronaldsway, served by this steam train service.

Far from being at the extreme edge of our islands, Ronaldsway enjoys a very central location. In fact, if you draw lines between Lerwick and Scilly, Malin Head and Sandetti and between Stornoway and Jersey, they intersect at Ronaldsway. So any way you look at it, this is a pretty central location. But it is also central to the Irish Sea, and so is an important source of weather data required for accurate forecasts. As such it could have been important from the very beginning of the weather forecasts produced by Robert Fitzroy. However, it does not appear on the very early lists of coastal stations, and it is unclear just when weather reports from the Isle of Man were first incorporated into the forecasting process. The weather station at Ronaldsway was established when the airfield was first opened in 1929. But for many years, the station collecting weather data for the Irish Sea was at Holyhead, always a major port.

Despite not visiting the Isle of Man for so many years, I did have a number of links with it. Not least of these was provided by reading of the *Bounty* voyage and discovering the connections that both Fletcher Christian and William Bligh had with the island. Having visited Christian's final home, on Pitcairn, where I stayed with some of his descendents, I was looking forward to finding out something more of his origins. By chance, the captain of the tallship *Soren Larsen* on my voyage to Pitcairn, Jim Cottier, was a native of Ramsey, a former industrial sea-port on the Isle of Man. When it came to planning my visit to the island, I wrote to Capt. Jim asking about his original home, and whether he knew of the whereabouts of Fletcher Christian's home. He supplied some valuable information. The Christian family home, Milntown, was not far from his childhood home in Ramsey, and he had cycled past it often, on his way to see a girlfriend who lived close-by. But he had never seen it! He remembered that it was surrounded by high

walls and tall trees and that the gates were always closed.    It
sounded quite a mystery.

Having agreed a basic plan with my friend Andy, it now fell to me
to plan the details. The chief constraint on timings turned out to be
the ferry between Douglas and Belfast. In the early spring, when
we hoped to travel, these are few and far between. If we were to
avoid a complicated series of ferries back and forth across the Irish
Sea, there was only one possible date to travel from Douglas to
Belfast directly. I could see how air travel had become so much
more popular. Fortunately there are more frequent ferries between
Liverpool and Douglas for the journey out and between Dublin and
Holyhead for the return.

This time I was able to avoid the usual early morning departure,
and met up with Andy on the train to London around midday.
Despite a rather overcrowded train from there to Liverpool, and a
complete lack of luggage space, the journey north was pleasant
enough. We were travelling very light in view of the number and
types of changes of transport we expected, but did feel sorry for
those trying to deal with cases and big rucksacks. Arriving at Lime
Street Station was quite a culture shock.  Asking for information,
directions and the taxi rank was easy enough, and the responses
were friendly, but I have to say, the Liverpool accent can seem
almost a parody of itself! It's difficult to take it all seriously, but
then they probably think the same about my accent.

A taxi took us to the ferry dock, though the ferry itself had not
arrived, so we had a couple of hours to explore before we would
board. By now the earlier rain had cleared and the sky brightened
into a perfect early spring afternoon.  We walked past the Royal
Liver Building to Albert Dock enjoying the newly redeveloped
quayside. This was another area of childhood travel memories.
The boat on which I travelled many times between Dublin and
Liverpool, universally known as the B&I (from British & Irish
Steam Packet Company), docked just beside the Royal Liver
Building. Many times I remember boarding the ship in the early

evening, and watching as the lock gates were opened to allow the ship out into the Mersey. The lock is gone, but there are reminders of it in the granite walls and kerbs that have been incorporated into the redevelopment.

Walking around the Albert Dock itself, in search of a coffee and a snack, we came across a lightship exhibit moored in the basin. A small notice identified it as the Planet, formerly the lightship at the bar of Liverpool port. After being replaced by a marine buoy it had done duty as none other than the Channel Light Vessel, between 1979 and 1989, when it had the distinction of being the last manned lightship operated on that station by Trinity House, the navigation lights authority for England and Wales[1]. Unfortunately there was no one aboard, and no suggestion of opening times, so we continued our stroll around the Dock.

Back at the ferry port, the catamaran *Snaefell* had docked, and we waited our turn to board in the passenger area. Our fellow passengers were a surprisingly mixed bunch, mixed origins, ages and sizes. And these were only the foot passengers, as cars with their drivers and passengers board separately. I could not help contrasting it with my experience of the Dunkirk ferry. But since it was not a school holiday, nor a particularly attractive time of year for taking holidays, I could only conclude that most were Isle of Man residents, perhaps returning from a shopping trip.

Soon after we had found our places, and collected a drink from the bar, we were on our way. The ferry pulled out past an incoming Mersey Ferry, into the main navigation channel. As it did so, I recollected that an installation by Antony Gormley should be visible as we headed out to sea. But at first I was not sure of where to look, knowing only that it consisted of a large number of cast-iron human form statues embedded in the sand, stretching out to sea. As we checked both banks, it became clear that it could only be on the North bank, and just as suddenly we caught sight of the first figures, staring out to sea, in the pale evening sunlight. I have to say they looked haunting and appealing at the same time. You could almost imagine them raising a cast-iron arm and waving a heavy-hearted farewell. Later, I checked on a web site, and found some details of the piece[2]. Its name is *Another Place* and it consists of 100 cast-iron, life-size figures, each one weighing 650 kilos, spread out along the foreshore, stretching almost one kilometre out to sea. Now a permanent feature at Crosby Beach, it was a surprise to me that it had previously been installed in Germany, Norway and Belgium. According to Antony Gormley, *Another Place* harnesses the ebb and flow of the tide to explore man's relationship with nature. He explains: "In this work human life is tested against planetary time. This sculpture exposes to light and time the nakedness of a particular and peculiar body. It is no hero, no ideal, just the industrially reproduced body of a middle-aged man trying to remain standing and trying to breathe, facing a horizon busy with ships moving materials and manufactured things around the planet."[3] I have to say, it worked for me, and that's a lot more than I can say for the food aboard the *Snaefell*. But perhaps his words, "no hero, no ideal, just industrially produced..." would be appropriate.

Out to sea, as the sun set, we passed many other installations, but these were dedicated to the search for, and production of, oil and gas from under the Irish Sea. On the passage to Douglas, it seemed that we were never far from their lights glowing brightly in the darkening sky.

By the time we arrived in Douglas it was quite late, and despite not eating well on the ferry we were not inclined to roam around looking for a meal. Instead, we left the ferry terminal, and walked along the damp, dark prom to find our hotel, just set back from the sea. We were warmly welcomed by the owner, and shown to our rooms at the top of the house. Douglas has a huge variety of B&B accommodation, much in traditional seaside terraces, partly why we chose the accommodation we did. If well maintained, and this was, and with some thoughtful modernisation of the plumbing, these can be very homely and comfortable, as well as great value.

In the morning, we awaited breakfast with trepidation. Recalling my childhood visits, I also recalled the smell of 'world famous' Manx Kippers! But alas our host declined to offer them, because of the lingering smell. Oh well, there was plenty else to set us up for the day. But first I introduced Andy to the 'Tea or Coffee' challenge. Perhaps for reasons of snobbery, but I claim because of the taste, I do not willingly drink instant coffee. So if I think an establishment will not offer fresh brewed coffee, I order tea. Andy guessed that such a nice place would not offer instant, but he was wrong and very disappointed! Not for the first time, I was highly amused, grinning as I drank my tea!

In preparation for the visit to Ronaldsway weather station I had thought it wise to make contact in advance. I was unlikely to be welcomed if I simply turned up at a busy airport asking to see the weather people. Fortunately the Isle of Man weather service has a fairly useful web site[4], which gives contact details of the staff and I had exchanged emails with Dr Alan Hisscott, the senior meteorological officer there. He was willing to entertain me, provided I had ID to pass through airport security. He explained that the weather station was in the control tower, a building dating from WW II, with few facilities. To contact him when I arrived, I should make myself known at the Airport Information Desk and he would come to escort me.

With the expectation of reasonable weather, we made our way to the train station, a delightful building, seemingly little changed from when it was first constructed well over one hundred years ago. The little engines have been operating for the same length of time, pulling the same carriages. Of course it has been much restored and renovated, but still has a very authentic appeal, though it runs largely as a tourist attraction. The timetable informs that Ronaldsway is a 'request' stop, so I informed the guard before we joined the train. I must confess myself very pleased to have been able to use the steam railway as part of my quest! In the early morning sunshine, the little green engine stood at the platform, its paint and brass gleaming, its cream and red wooden carriages sparkling. On inspection, I saw the engine was one of the newer ones, built in Manchester in 1905! Everything was so small, from the three foot track gauge to the low carriage doors. Standing in the compartments was impossible, but the ancient fittings, brass handles, leather strap to raise the window, wooden roof, more than made up for the probability of banging my head.

Right on time, with a loud whistle, the train pulled out of the station, past the workshops and the yards needed to maintain such a working museum. The semaphore signals, smell of smoke and clouds of steam passing the window all added to the delight. We climbed steadily out of Douglas, crossed little valleys and roads as we slowly made our way out into the countryside. The fields and trackside were ablaze with gorse and spring flowers. At Ballasalla, some 30 minutes later, the train drew into a station with two platforms, and stopped. Moments later, another train appeared from the south and drew into the other platform. As the two engines drew level, each driver leaned out and passed a 'token' to the other. These are the antique methods by which railway safety is assured, since the driver is only permitted to take the train onto the next, single line, section if in possession of the correct 'token'.

My stop was the next one, and as communicated to the guard, the train duly stopped while I alone got off. Andy had declined to visit the actual weather station, and was staying on the train to Port Erin, the end of the line. We would meet up again later, either in Port Erin, or back at the hotel in Douglas.

It was only a short walk, across a stile, along a quiet track and past an eye-catching sculpture of the Manx three legs symbol, to the airport terminal building. Much of this was new, but some of the façade seemed to be older, much older than the rest of the building. Perhaps it was here in the days that I travelled as a child. At the information desk, as instructed, I asked for Dr Alan Hisscott, and was pleased to find that I was expected. Alan came to meet me and we passed through the normal airport security. "It was very different in the old days," said Alan, "there was no security at all, and we each had a key to the airport terminal. We used to lock up

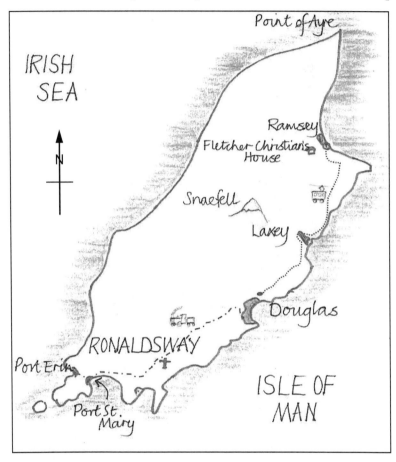

as we left." I followed my host through the buildings and out to the base of the old control tower. A new control tower is under construction, and when it is completed the weather station will move to new premises. The existing WWII building is too hot in summer and too cold in winter, so the staff will be pleased to make the move. But they will still have to exit and enter through airport security.

The weather recording instruments are on the other side of the runway, but easily visible from Alan's office, in which three or four individuals sit in front of computer screens. There is no need for any of the staff to directly read the instruments. They all have remote readouts in the office. When I arrived, a technician was inspecting some of the equipment. On hearing of my quest, he told me that he was at one time based at Malin Head, and sometimes still visited that site to inspect and service their instruments. Like many of the staff that I met at the different stations, he had served at many different posts around the UK and overseas.

Sitting at one of the desks, behind a large microphone, was Bob, to whom I was introduced as the voice of the weather on Isle of Man radio. The weather forecast is delivered to Isle of Man residents directly from the weather station. Bob explained that they also have a premium line where anyone can call the weather station, and are able to speak to a forecaster. I wondered what kind of questions people asked. "Oh, all sorts, you'd be surprised. Sometimes people call up about the state of the sea, before taking a ferry. Sometimes people want to know if they should put their washing out. I've had people call to pass the time," said Bob. "But the funniest was a woman who saw all these premium rate calls on her husband's telephone bill and wondered what he had been doing. Perhaps she imagined strange girls on the other end of the line, but he was a fisherman and all he was doing was checking the forecast."

Like Jersey, the Isle of Man has its own weather service. This was part of the MOD until 1966, but since then it has been a department of government in the Isle of Man. The RAF no longer use Ronaldsway on a regular basis, but originally it was established as an airbase. Its time as a weather station dates from then.

I asked if they kept any of the old instruments, and was told that they continue to keep records made with their Campbell-Stokes sunshine recorder, since the modern sunshine recorders use a different technique, and so record hours of sunshine slightly differently. For the sake of the continuous record going forward, and to avoid errors generated by a change of instrumentation, they continue with the Campbell-Stokes records. The different recording methods used by the new instruments can give rise to erroneous interpretation of trends, when compared with the older recording methods. However, for the most part, the readings recorded by the automatic equipment are those used, and forwarded to the Met Office, and colleagues around the world.

The Campbell-Stokes recorder is very simple and elegant, and has been in use for a long time. Its main constituent is a glass sphere, about the size of a grapefruit, and looking remarkably like a crystal ball. The function of the sphere is to focus sunlight, from any angle, on a specially made cardboard strip wrapped around the sphere. When the sun shines, the focussed sunlight scorches a small hole in the cardboard, which then continues as a scorched trace as the sun tracks across the sky. When there is no sun, there is a gap in the track on the card. By reading the scorch marks against a calibrated scale, it is fairly straightforward to count up the hours of sunlight. But this is time consuming, and cannot be automated, so more modern instruments judge the sunshine by recording the solar energy measured continuously throughout the day. The measurements made by the two different types of instrument rarely agree.

I asked Alan if they had recorded weather changes that could be attributed to climate change. He said that climate change, and in particular sea level rise, would clearly have an impact on the Isle of Man, but the one effect they have noticed to date is on tidal surges. Placed at the centre of the Irish Sea, the Isle of Man is particularly susceptible to weather-induced tidal surges. So increases in sea level, and in extreme weather conditions, are likely to intensify the effects of these surges in the future, leading to increased flooding, particularly of the low-lying northern areas.

The staff were interested to hear of my visits to other coastal stations, and of my own experiences of recording weather data on board ship, far from land in the South Pacific Ocean. We discussed the need to verify predictions and forecasts, and of the limited amounts of data available from the seas, far from shipping routes. I told them of my visit to Pitcairn, and staying with the descendants of Fletcher Christian. I feel sure that weather observations are made on Pitcairn and other inhabited islands in the South Pacific, but I must confess I did not ask during my visit there.

Before I left, I asked for a weather forecast for the remainder of my visit, and for our onward travel to Belfast in two days' time. I was given a readout which looked quite hopeful for good weather, but with a possibility of showers. To illustrate the forecast, Bob showed me some pictures which are sent every 5 minutes from Meteosat, the European Space Agency weather satellite focused on Western Europe. Receiving the images from the satellite used to cost tens of thousands of pounds, but they are now available from Sky Digital, for a very modest fee.

With my visit over, Alan escorted me back through airport security. On the way I asked about the original terminal, and Alan confirmed that the older sections of the building would have been there when I came as a child. I also noticed something I had missed on the way in. Many of the airport signs are written in the Manx language, as well as English. As with Scotland and Wales, and indeed Ireland, there is a language revival underway in the Isle of Man. Manx has all but died out as a spoken language, but many of the records and archives of the Isle of Man are in Manx. Schoolchildren now learn some Manx during their schooling, and there are occasional programmes in the Manx language on radio. As a written language, it resembles Irish Gaelic, and from what I see it is mainly understandable by a reader of Irish Gaelic.

Back at the Ronaldsway train station, I joined another passenger waiting to flag down the train to Port Erin. He introduced himself as an engineer finishing his shift on aircraft maintenance at the airport. His wife would shortly arrive on the Douglas bound train, he would pass her the car keys, she would go to work at the airport for her shift on check-in while he took the train to St Mary's that would arrive some 5 minutes later. It seemed a strangely Manx version of Brief Encounter. The trains duly arrived, the keys were exchanged, and I boarded for the short journey on to Port Erin.

I remember many things of Port Erin from my childhood, the little harbour, the headland with the tower on the top, the beach and what I'd taken to be a lighthouse in the middle of the beach. Looking at the scene now, it was almost exactly as I remember from perhaps 55 years ago. There were changes however: the row of guesthouses that wound its way up from the beach towards the headland was gone. In its place was a line of apartment buildings, some new build replacing older property, others simply converting the existing guesthouses to new purpose. I looked for the aquarium near the fishing harbour where I had seen and marvelled at fish being hatched and reared for study. In particular I remember learning there how plaice start life. Hatching, they look like ordinary fish, with an eye on either side of their body. As they grow, one side changes to a darker colour, the other lighter, while one eye migrates to the other side of the fish's body, and the growing plaice becomes a tiny version of the flatfish we recognise. But alas, the aquarium, for many years managed by Liverpool University, had closed.

Returning to the beach, and I could now see what was not clear to a child. What I had taken to be a lighthouse on the beach was in fact a leading light, used to guide boats safely toward the harbour. Across the beach flowed a small stream, as it did so many years ago. Damning this stream with a sand barrage provided endless fascination to me, to my brother and our various playmates. Along from the river, at the base of the leading light, I found the Cosy Nook Cafe, just as it was. By an odd coincidence, on my return home our local newspaper, The Dorking Advertiser[5] which includes an almost pastiche cafe review, chose this week to review the Cosy Nook Cafe.

Next day we had decided to take the Manx Electric Railway to Ramsey. Dr Hisscott had explained to me that the Electric Railway had been built because there was electricity available during the day. When the first electricity generator was built on the Isle of Man, the main requirement for electricity was for lighting at night. But the Douglas City Council would not permit the Electric Railway to run to the centre of Douglas, and required it to terminate at the north end of the promenade. Passengers wishing to travel to the centre of Douglas could then take a horse tram for the last part of their journey. It seems many of the original passengers would have been miners on their way to or from work in the mines at Laxey, travelling from either Douglas or Ramsey at the far end of the railway. Nowadays the railway mainly serves tourists, and in the summer runs special coaches with open sides. Instead of taking miners to Laxey, it takes tourists to join the Snaefell mountain railway to the summit of the island's highest mountain.

However, summer had not quite arrived because we woke up to a steady and persistent rain. This was not as had been forecast; the 'possible showers' had organised themselves into real rain. But we walked the length of the promenade ignoring the rain, since the horse trams service had not yet started for the summer season, and boarded the Electric Rail car to Ramsey. There we hoped to see where my friend Capt. Jim had lived as a child and maybe find out something of Fletcher Christian's house.

Like the Steam Railway, the Manx Electric Railway is much restored and rebuilt, so the carriages, looking a little like tram cars, made largely of wood and steel, are beautifully preserved. Even after 100 years, they look serviceable and attractive, the wood carefully varnished and the paint bright and shining in the drizzle. But it is slow, taking 75 minutes to cover the 18 miles to Ramsey. Again the words of Robert Louis Stevenson, "to travel hopefully is a better thing than to arrive", came to mind.  The railway tracks run partly alongside the road, and give super views towards the wild coast, across small fields used for mixed farming, much like in Ireland.

The idea of the Isle of Man as a mining and industrial centre is quite at odds with our current ideas of a tax-haven, seaside holiday centre and retirement destination.   But Laxey was a significant mining village and the Laxey mines produced a steady supply of copper, lead, silver and zinc ore from ancient times until the mine closed in 1929.  The famous Laxey Big Wheel used water power to grind ore, pump water from the mine and to lift miners' cages and mine trucks to the surface.  Ramsey too was an industrial port, taking the ores produced at Laxey and elsewhere on the Isle of Man overseas for smelting.  With their Viking heritage, Manx people have always been regarded as good sailors, so it's no surprise that many from here made a career at sea.  Significant shipbuilding took place at Ramsey, and in fact the world's oldest functioning sailing ship, the *Star of India*, was built here in 1863.  Unusually for the time she was built largely of iron, a novelty which probably helped her survive till the present day.  In 1871 she embarked on a quarter century of hauling emigrants to New Zealand, sometimes also touching Australia, California and Chile.   She made 21 circumnavigations in this service, some of them lasting up to a year.  But the days of sail were limited, and in 1901 she was bought by an Alaska cannery where she remained in use as a floating warehouse until rescued and restored in recent years.

Laxey today still has the air of a mining village with the houses tucked in to the side of the hill, climbing steadily up around the edge of the valley.  For train buffs it is also the start of the third of the Isle of Man's historic railways, the Snaefell Mountain Railway, which goes to the top of Snaefell, the islands highest mountain.  I recall that we took this trip on one holiday, and remember looking out across the high moors to the coasts of the island, and across the sea to the Mourne Mountains.  Amongst our fellow passengers there were lots of takers for the trip, though mist and cloud came down to a couple of hundred feet. There would be no views across the Irish Sea today.

In Ramsey we warmed up with a cup of coffee and set off through the steady drizzle to find Capt. Jim's house. I took some pictures to send to him, and from there we followed his directions to look for Fletcher Christian's house. Just as he had described, we found the high walls and the high trees that surrounded the house. But the gate was open! Looking down the driveway from the gate, it was clear that significant work was in progress on the house. A large sign said 'Private Property Keep out' and Andy was rather shocked when I suggested we simply walk in. There were lots of trades people about, some putting up scaffolding, some fairly busy inside the house. I asked one of them about the house and he confirmed that it was indeed Fletcher Christian's family home. He pointed to the gable and showed us the Christian family crest. Most recently, it had belonged to Sir Clive Edwards, Bart. who had left it in trust to the people of the Isle of Man. The work underway was to enable it to open to the public, adding a tea shop and also a museum to house some of Sir Clive's collection of motorbikes. Opening[6] was scheduled for the summer season, and though we could not go into the house because of the work underway there, we did see some of the collection of motorbikes. Perhaps I could schedule a future visit, maybe with Paul or my brother, to see the house.

Back in Douglas that afternoon I went to the museum. They must have many enquiries about Fletcher Christian and also about William Bligh who, though not a Manxman, had worked from Douglas aboard a customs cutter. Bligh had recruited Christian to sail with him aboard *Britannia* to the West Indies sometime before the notorious *Bounty* voyage. They probably became acquainted through Bligh's wife, who came from Douglas. The library has lots of materials concerning Bligh, Christian and also Peter Heyward, another Manxman caught up in the *Bounty* mutiny. The story of that mutiny, its aftermath on Pitcairn and Bligh's epic voyage under sail to East Timor, is much more interesting and exciting than any

Hollywood portrayal. A distant relative, Glynn Christian, wrote a book called *Fragile Paradise*[7] which tells the story of life on Pitcairn with the mutineers settled. Another account by Trevor Lummus, *Life and Death in Eden*[8] gives a comprehensive view of the whole Pitcairn saga based on an oft forgotten source. One of the Polynesian women taken to Pitcairn by the mutineers, known as 'Jenny', told her story to missionaries on Tahiti, where she returned after Pitcairn had re-established contact with the outside world. Much of the legend about the mutiny and life on Pitcairn is based on stories told by John Adams, the only mutineer left alive when American whalers re-discovered the island. Adams told many different accounts of the mutiny and events afterwards at different times, probably because as a mutineer he risked hanging, and was almost certainly involved in murder on the island. Jenny's account is consistent and likely to be a more accurate source, since by the time she gave it she was away from the island and away from any influence by Adams. As is the way, the woman's story is often neglected, particularly when the woman concerned was a 'native'. But it makes compelling reading.

Fletcher was the seventh child, and third son, of a family who made their home in Cockermouth in Cumbria, where he attended the same school as William Wordsworth. The move to Ramsey took place after the death of Fletcher's father, when his mother was very short of money and so returned to the Isle of Man to live with family members. As a third son, Fletcher would not have had any expectation of inheriting land, and so a career at sea would have been attractive to him and to his family. Ironically, none of his siblings had children, so he would indeed have inherited. During his time as a customs officer, Bligh would have sailed the waters of the Irish Sea and must have known Dublin well. Later in his career he designed the large works that protect the harbour in Dublin and through which Paul and I had travelled on our way home from Valentia. The third *Bounty* crew member with Isle of Man connections, Peter Heywood, came from a very influential family, which ensured that Bligh's account of the mutiny was challenged. Heywood himself left the *Bounty* in Tahiti, was captured by the navy ship *Pandora* and was returned to England for trial. Though found guilty of mutiny, with his family's influence he was pardoned and returned to the navy, where he had a very distinguished career which included action with Nelson.

Before leaving Douglas, I found a large card to send to my friend Capt. Jim, in New Zealand, with news of his childhood home and our view of the Fletcher Christian house which he never got to see. Pictures would follow later. All in all I was delighted with my visit to the island, and on the final evening we celebrated in suitable style at the best restaurant we could find. The morning would see us up early and on the ferry to Belfast for our onward journey to Malin Head.

---

[1] For information see www.feuerschiffseite.de a source of lots of Lightship information.

[2] See AntonyGormley.com.

[3] Quoted from VisitLiverpool.com.

[4] www.gov.im/infocentre/weather.aspx.

[5] www.thisissurreytoday.co.uk/news/Cosy-Nook-Cafe-Port-Erin-Isle-Man/article-996671-detail/article.html.

[6] Now open, see www.milntown.org.

[7] *Fragile Paradise*, by Glynn Christian, published 1996 by Penguin.

[8] *Life and Death in Eden* by Trevor Lummus, published 1999 by Penguin.

# Malin Head

55° 22′ N       7° 20′ W

South southeast 6, 8 miles, 1006, Now rising

May 2009

The visit to Malin Head was planned to follow on from the Ronaldsway visit. Early in the year there are very few ferries from Douglas to Belfast, so this crossing was in effect the linchpin of both journeys. Missing this early morning ferry would entail a complicated series of trials back and forth across the Irish Sea. In fact there really had been nothing stopping me making the visit to Malin Head as part of any of my regular visits to Ireland to see my mother, but combining the two weather stations seemed to make for a more rewarding journey. As it was, I would visit my mother on the return journey through Dublin. To assist our early start, the hotel had left a packed breakfast for us to take on our journey. Sir William Hillary, the originator of the idea for RNLI, the Royal National Lifeboat Institution, lived here in Douglas. He was instrumental in two 'have-a-go' sea rescues in the waters nearby before the first lifeboat was stationed here. Not many people were about as we walked to the terminal along the promenade past the monument to Sir William and his achievements.

Nor did many passengers join the ferry before the doors were closed and the staff advised we should expect a bumpy ride at first, though this should improve as we passed the northernmost part of the island. So it was, when we turned west, having passed Point of Ayre, the sea calmed considerably though by this time many of the passengers had been seasick, and using the lavatory was a very unpleasant experience.

Before very much longer, however, we were travelling up Belfast Lough and spotted the massive Harland &Wolff crane which dominates the skyline of downtown Belfast. Shipbuilding has long since ceased in Belfast, but in former times it was a major engineering centre, not just building ships but also aircraft. Harland & Wolff is probably most famous as the builder of the *Titanic*, and in a major shift of fortunes, that ship's unfortunate fate is now to be the centre for a new exhibition. This is planned to open in 2012 to coincide with the 100th anniversary of *Titanic's* maiden voyage and sinking. Looking carefully at that now derelict shipyard you can just distinguish the former slipways from which the ships, including *Titanic*, were launched. These dramatic ceremonies are no longer performed, as almost all shipbuilding now takes place by constructing major segments of the ship in dockside factories and then assembling them in a large dry dock, using giant cranes like that now redundant example preserved here. Instead, we have naming ceremonies, where the obligatory bottle of champagne is broken on the bow of an already floating ship, a pale imitation of a launch ceremony. Fortunately we have newsreel film of the drama that accompanied the launch of many famous ships, with the final wedge knocked away before the ship rumbled steadily into the water.

It's not possible to arrive in Belfast without being aware of the unfortunate history of Northern Ireland. We consider this goes back to 1968 with the start of the Northern Ireland Civil Rights movement but in reality it goes back much further. In 1922 Ireland was partitioned, the South eventually becoming the Republic of Ireland, whilst the North remained part of the United Kingdom.

But the partition has its anomalies. Malin Head, the most northerly part of Ireland, is part of the Republic. It sticks out well north of any part of Northern Ireland. On such a prominent headland you might expect to find a prominent lighthouse, but there is none. Just a little further north of the headland is a series of dangerous rocks, Tor Rocks, so shipping needing to clear Malin Head also needs to

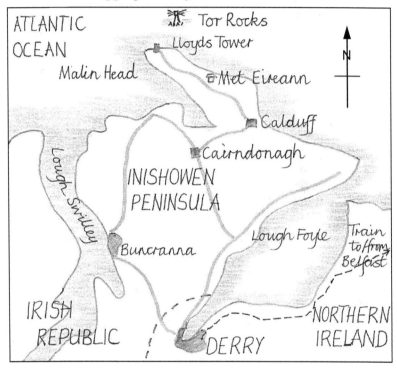

keep clear of these rocks. Ireland's most northerly lighthouse is situated here, on an islet called Inishtrahaul.

Thankfully 'the troubles', as Irish people refer to the bloody conflict with characteristic understatement, are fading into history and investment is brightening up the once bomb-damaged cities of Northern Ireland. Around the docks in Belfast, as in most other cities, harbour-side apartments are being built to replace derelict warehouses.  With these comes public investment too, Belfast's Waterside Hall is now a fixture on the international concert circuit, and public money has improved the transport infrastructure.  New buildings and new roads are everywhere.  There is a new Central Station, which serves decent coffee, and has free, very clean, toilets.  There are not many main railway stations that can offer as much.

But buying a ticket can still be fraught with difficulties for a stranger.  And though I am Irish, coming from the south I still feel a stranger in Belfast.  Checking information and timetables on the web, I noticed that the train schedule referred to the 'Belfast to Londonderry' service, while the bus schedule showed the final destination as Derry.  During 'the troubles', how you referred to the city could cause or save considerable problems.  In the Republic any road sign will only signpost 'Derry', whilst in the North I only saw 'Londonderry'.  Some people attempt to be politically correct by referring to London/Derry while others humorously talk of 'Stroke City'.  Personally, because of my past, I find it difficult to say anything but Derry, and fortunately the ticket clerk had no problem with that.

The rain and drizzle continued as we left Belfast but by the time we pulled out of Coleraine on the north coast, the sun was breaking through and we had a really pleasant journey around the coast, with its famous golf courses, and along the Foyle Estuary to Derry station, just across the river from the old city.  Derry is the only city in Ireland to have a complete set of city walls, rare enough anywhere in Europe.  Perhaps when memories of the recent history that unfolded there have faded, there will be more opportunity to celebrate this unique fortification.  For the present, however, the walls of Derry have political significance that is alive to this day.  For the Orangemen they represent the stand Derry took against the Catholic King James, withstanding a long siege before relief was sent by the Protestant King William and the city was held.  For the Nationalist community they represent hundreds of years of domination by the other community.

But for us the Walls of Derry proved an irresistible stroll and a vantage point to look down on the Bogside district and some of the remaining iconography of the troubles. From here you can see 'Free Derry Corner' and many gable end paintings, mostly now celebrating the end of the 'armed struggle' with broken rifles a feature. Palestinian flags flew in places alongside Irish Republican flags, suggesting common cause in adversity. Andy was amazed by the spectacle. Like many people in England, he had heard of the 'troubles' in Northern Ireland, but they always seemed distant. Seeing it up close was unsettling.

Despite being a Thursday, inside the city walls and particularly around the shopping areas, the streets were full of crop-haired, greased young men, accompanied by fat girls with bulging midriffs. Most were smoking, and exhaling an air of menace with the cigarette smoke. Personally I found this more scary than anything I had seen from the city walls. And in case you should imagine the troubles have completely ceased, on the bus leaving Derry we passed the Strand Road Police Station, built like a fortress, high fences topped with barbed wire, watchtowers, CCTV, clearly indicating a police force still under siege. Since our visit, and despite the fortifications, the station came under bomb and mortar attack from Republican dissidents again.

Aboard the bus with us was a very odd collection of passengers, including a man with six bottles of vodka in a supermarket plastic bag. He explained that vodka was much cheaper in Northern Ireland, but the bottles clanked dangerously for the whole journey. Many other passengers had large packages and bags of shopping. Those living near the border between the Republic and Northern Ireland have always had opportunities to cross back and forth taking advantage of the differing prices on either side. Now with the constantly changing euro/sterling exchange rate, and differing excise duties, there are plenty of possible shopping opportunities available. In the past there was an actual border post on this road, and our fellow passenger would have been taking a risk crossing with his six bottles of vodka.  But the border was always very porous, with many unapproved road crossings, ideal for small and large-scale smuggling.

Now the border is almost invisible, just a change of road surface and a new speed limit sign, indicating 50 kph (The Republic is metric, but Northern Ireland isn't.)  There is little else to suggest a frontier.  As I craned my neck to catch a glimpse of anything that might indicate the border, a lady passenger behind me pointed out the remains of a customs post, tucked away and overgrown at the side of the road.

The bus took us to the Diamond in Cairndonagh, a pleasant space in a very pleasant Irish village.  We phoned ahead to confirm our arrival time, having previously arranged through the tourist office to hire bikes.  Phelan, the owner of the bike hire business, arrived in a van with the bikes and helmets, then produced locks when we requested them.  He thought them unnecessary and explained his locks would in any case only keep an honest thief away!  He asked us to leave the bikes behind the chemist shop, unlocked, when we had finished with them.

Our accommodation had been booked at Calduff, a small village about 8 km beyond Cairndonagh on an unexpectedly busy road.  But we soon turned off to reach another very attractive but smaller, quiet village.  After our busy day we were pleased to reach the B&B, called simply 'Village House', and enjoyed a very welcome afternoon tea provided by the owner, Joan.  At her suggestion we explored the coast and wonderful beaches just outside the village.  It was beautiful in the evening sunshine, but though calm, the Atlantic waters looked very cold.

In the morning, we filled up with a good breakfast, and then set off for the final kilometres to Malin Head!  The morning forecast said it would be wet until around 10, then sunny for the rest of the day.  Though it was sunny as we left the village, soon we were cycling through a heavy rain shower.  We managed to avoid the busy roads of yesterday and cycled along narrow lanes through pretty countryside near the sea. Being spring, the hedgerows were ablaze with gorse, hawthorn and primroses. The only downside was the number of cottages, mostly new, that had been constructed in the recent past, a symptom of Ireland's property boom. Perhaps surprisingly, even on these small lanes, Malin Head was well signposted. From leaving the village, we had about a 20 km cycle, and by the time we had passed a couple of schools and a big wind turbine, we rounded a bend and saw lots of masts, then quite suddenly the sign, 'Met Eireann, Malin Head.' We had arrived.

We posed by the sign for photos then I suggested we knock at the front door. "You cannot just walk in," said Andy. Oh yes I can, I was thinking as I approached the door and found a key in the lock. I knocked and when a voice answered "Come in" I had the feeling we might have been expected. But no, the key had been left in the door as the Post was expected, so I introduced myself and asked if I could come in for a chat about the weather station. Martin, clearly the boss, responded, "Well it's a working station, you know, but I suppose it's OK for a minute. What can we do for you?" I explained about the quest and Martin's initial stiffness evaporated. We were offered tea and discussed, as two Irish people meeting anywhere in the world would do, our origins. Martin originally came from Dublin, and had lived very close to where I was brought up. Perhaps we had even played together. His young colleague, Ruth, was working at a screen, and explained that she was submitting the hourly observation data at that very moment. When she had finished, we discussed the weather, the morning's forecast, and the heavy shower we had encountered on the way. Martin showed us a screen displaying the weather map derived from the radar which detects approaching rain. Malin Head is just off this radar map so forecasting rain for the local area is more difficult than for areas further east.

The weather station will soon be automated, and work was already in progress to enable this to happen. I wondered what the staff would do following the automation. But there is plenty of work to do at Met Eireann's head office in Dublin, and not enough staff to do it. Ruth for one was looking forward to the move to Dublin. At the moment, they work 12 hours on, then 12 hours off, for three days then have four days leave. Not surprisingly Ruth finds Malin Head very dull, and leaves for Dublin as soon as her shift is finished. The view from the weather station is wonderful, but I think I too would find it paled after a time. Martin claimed proudly that during the summer, on a clear day they can see the sun rise over the Paps of Jura. Later I checked and found this to be some 35 miles away, not an unreasonable distance from which to see the sunrise.

Before we left, Ruth showed us the instruments outside. Like the station at Ronaldsway, Malin Head retains its sunshine records from the Campbell-Stokes recorder. When the station is automated, this record will cease. We climbed to the roof to check the instrument, and then said our goodbyes and thanks. Ruth seemed genuinely happy that we had called. "It's lonely here you know," she said, "so we're pleased to have the bit of excitement, in fact, you made our day!" And it's not every day a young lady says that to me.

The weather station is a few kilometres short of Malin Head itself, so after a few more pictures, we continued out to the point. This is Ireland's John O'Groats, the most northerly point of the island. The southern extreme is Mizen Head, in County Cork, not so far from Valentia. At the headland we found the tower which Martin had told us about. It was originally built in 1805 to guard against a landing by Napoleon. Later it was taken over and used by Lloyd's of London to make contact with passing shipping and receive messages for onward transmission to ship owners and the market. At first, messages were passed by semaphore signals, spotted through a telescope. These would have been relayed by telegraph when that became available, but it was not until 1902 that the Marconi company built a wireless transmitter at the site. Even then, wireless would have been a rarity on ships, so the semaphore and telescope communication continued for some time afterwards.

Though I can find no direct evidence, Fitzroy's signals must have been displayed from here, and the Lloyd's tower was probably the source of his observations in this area. Malin Head figures on an early list of Coastal Stations[1], and the adjacent sea area, Malin, attests to its importance to shipping throughout the history of weather forecasting.

Though I have not yet found evidence to support my conjecture, there must have been a similar arrangement near Falmouth, possibly on the Lizard, to obtain reports from arriving shipping. 'To Falmouth, for orders,' was the almost universal command to captains of merchant vessels leaving distant ports for Europe. With no wireless communication, the first the captain and crew would know of the final destination of their cargo would be received as they arrived off Falmouth. As I described in the Greenwich chapter, the cargo, and possibly the vessel too, may have been changed hands many times during the voyage. This practice was still in operation as late as 1939, when Eric Newby arrived off Falmouth aboard *Moshulu* after his epic voyage from South Australia[2].

Visible from the Lloyd's Tower, a giant 'EIRE' sign is picked out with white stones on the grass below. This dates from WWII, when Eire, southern Ireland, was neutral, and I imagine the purpose of the sign was to alert combat aircraft to their location. I'm pretty sure it did little to deter over-flights from the nearby Ballykelly RAF base in Northern Ireland. But there was a good deal of unacknowledged support for the Allied cause in Ireland, particularly after the US became involved. My father, along with many tens of thousands from the south, signed up for the British forces during the war. Initially he had the good fortune to be posted to Northern Ireland, before embarking for Europe after D-Day. On all his home leaves he, like his colleagues travelling to Eire, changed out of uniform at the port, and changed back again on his return, a practice that satisfied the minimum requirements of Irish neutrality.

On our way back to Calduff, my bike began making horrid grinding noises from the crank, and I feared being stranded. When a group of professional looking cyclists appeared over the brow of a hill, I hoped they might carry tools to help. Though sympathetic, they didn't have the right tool. They were doing Ireland end-to-end, Mizen Head to Malin Head, having previously done Lands End to John O'Groats. They relied on car back-up, provided by a helpful wife, but she was having a day off as they neared their destination. Fortunately the crank held out, but fearful that it may collapse in the morning as we sprinted for the bus, I rang Phelan, who was happy for us to leave the bikes in Calduff so that we could take the bus from there. Actually he would have been happy to drive out with a replacement had we not been so near the end of our trip.

Calduff, though tiny, has a well deserved reputation as a centre for Irish music, specifically in the backroom of McGrory's pub. So that would be our evening's destination before the journey home. First we enjoyed a superb meal in the front room of the pub, served by one of the McGrory clan. He was most welcoming and insisted we should stay on after the meal for the session, which would start around 10 pm.

When we moved into the backroom, we were a little surprised to find a large group of young men, noisily engaged in innocent fun, but drinking heavily. It seemed unlikely they had come for the session. But there were few others in the bar as the musicians arrived in ones and twos. Soon there was quite a collection of instruments being taken from their cases and tuned: two fifes, a squeeze box, a guitar and several fiddles. But the drinking lads, though mellow, showed no inclination to listen quietly, continuing a raucous banter throughout. Which is a pity since the musicians were very good, and clearly enjoyed playing together. But again I was quite foxed by the way the music developed. It seems each instrument takes a lead in turn, with the other instruments joining in and adding their own detail. The result is enjoyable, but to my untrained ear, I have to say that most of the tunes sound similar.

We enjoyed the music for a while but with the noise from our drinking friends increasing all the time we decided it would be a good move to head off to bed before a fight broke out!

In the morning, I walked around the village before the bus arrived. I was interested to find an Anglican, Church of Ireland, church, but no Roman Catholic church. This is not unusual in Donegal but would be unusual in the rest of the Republic. Apart from the drinking lads in the pub the previous night, everything we had seen in Donegal was peaceful and friendly, a very distinct difference from my feeling about Derry. But when I came across the village telephone box, I was amazed to see it had been comprehensively vandalised; the glass lay scattered about, the receiver had been ripped from the phone and lay smashed on the ground, and the phone itself looked as though it had been hit by a brick. I could not say if this had happened the previous night, but clearly there is a violent streak below the friendly surface.

Our bus took us first to the county town, Letterkenny, where we changed for a Dublin bound bus. By now we were leaving the wilder parts of Donegal, where gorse, turf cutting and cattle predominate and moving into the more fertile parts of the county. Ireland has a real problem with planning laws as evidenced by the building we saw everywhere. New cottages, many of which were designed like little palaces, were scattered like confetti over the countryside. I could not imagine what so many people would do in this area. Even as holiday homes they would have limited attraction. It seems my worry about the viability of this property boom was well founded, and now one of the legacies of Ireland's 'Celtic Tiger' economy is unsold and unsaleable properties throughout the country.

Our journey took us back into Northern Ireland, again with no evident border. But the look of the countryside was different, and it took me a while to realise that this was because of the absence of houses scattered freely over the countryside. It seems that in

Northern Ireland planning restrictions work. The route took us through Omagh, a name it is impossible to hear without associations with the bomb. We stopped there briefly and moved out of the centre again with just a glimpse of the notorious High Street. At last, we crossed back into the Republic and joined the new M1 to Dublin Airport. Andy, despite his green credentials, was not subject to the same restrictions on travel as me. He would leave for home courtesy of Ryanair whilst I would stay in Dublin for three days to visit and hopefully entertain my mother, who lived in a care home not far from the airport.

When my turn came to leave, I joined the Irish Ferries ship *Jonathan Swift* in the port of Dublin bound for Holyhead. From there it was a relatively quiet and simple journey home by train. I had time on the journey to reflect on the weather stations I had visited, and my progress with the quest. So far I'd managed seven of the thirteen stations, so I had six more to go. I had taken six years to get this far, would it take me another six years to complete my quest? I hoped not.

---

[1] Met Office History, available from www.metoffice.org.uk.

[2] *The Last Grain Race*, by Eric Newby, published by Picador.

Left: Author at the Channel Lightship.

Below: Searching for Sandettie in the gloom.

Above: Busy bridge of a channel ferry.

Right: Simon, the *Fearless II* captain.

Left: Flamborough Head, North Shore.

Below: Sending the weather report, from Bridlington.

Left: All I ask is a tallship – *Europa!*

Below: *Europa* at anchor in the Azores.

Left: Climbing the mast by day, practice to spot the Greenwich light at night.

Above: Maison St. Louis, the original Jersey weather station.

Left: Ginny in the Jersey weather station.

Right: Valentia, the balloon goes up!

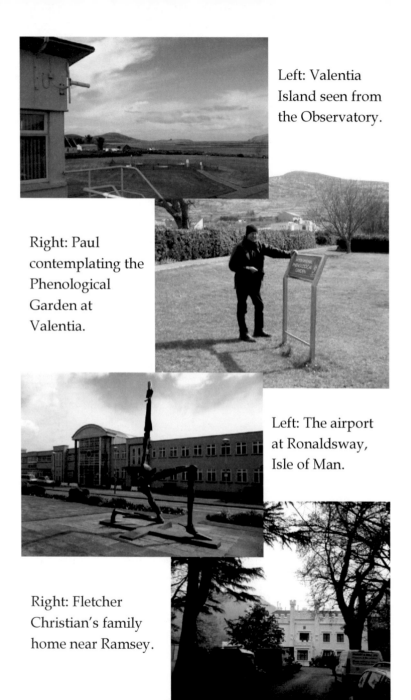

Left: Valentia Island seen from the Observatory.

Right: Paul contemplating the Phenological Garden at Valentia.

Left: The airport at Ronaldsway, Isle of Man.

Right: Fletcher Christian's family home near Ramsey.

Below: The Met
Eireann weather
station at Malin Head.

Above: Brief
Encounter at
Ronaldsway station

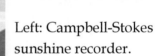

Left: Campbell-Stokes
sunshine recorder.

Right: Phantom IV,
retired plane at the
RAF Leuchars base.

Left: Alec preparing the weather report at RAF Leuchars.

Below: Stornoway harbour.

**TESCO**

Fosgailte
Open
Diluain - Dihaoine 6m - 12f
Disathairne 6m - 10f
Mon to Fri 6am - 12pm
Sat 6am - 10pm

Ath-chuartachagh
Recycling

Crannchur
Lottery

Biadh Fionnair
Delicatessen

Above: Even Tesco use Gaelic.

Right: Peter preparing the ozone sampling package.

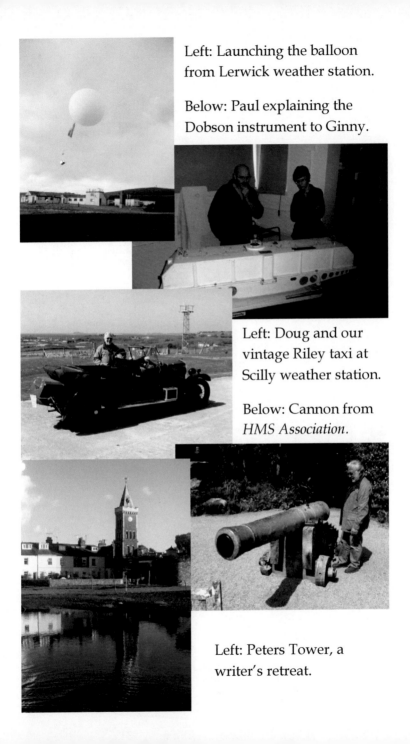

Left: Launching the balloon from Lerwick weather station.

Below: Paul explaining the Dobson instrument to Ginny.

Left: Doug and our vintage Riley taxi at Scilly weather station.

Below: Cannon from *HMS Association*.

Left: Peters Tower, a writer's retreat.

Above: Andy enjoying
the journey to Tiree.

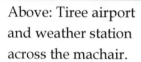

Above: Tiree airport
and weather station
across the machair.

Above: With Mary, my
companion to Greenwich.

Left: Mick and *Royal
Charlotte;* my passage to
Sandettie.

Below: The elusive
Sandettie at last!

# Leuchars

56° 23′ N        2° 52′ W

West southwest 5, 25 miles, Fair, 1002, Rising

August 2009

This was always going to be a challenge. For a start, during the years of my quest, it replaced a more familiar name, Fife Ness. Looking at the map, the co-ordinates given on the BBC website, and satellite pictures, it became obvious that the weather station must be on the RAF airbase of the same name. How would I be able to arrange to visit an RAF airbase? From the information I was able to glean, Leuchars is a front line base, with aircraft ready for dispatch at short notice to intercept 'hostile' intruders. Formerly, I suppose, that would have been the Soviet aircraft that wandered not so aimlessly around the fringes of NATO airspace. Chillingly, I suspect it now includes the readiness to shoot down hi-jacked planes that are deemed to pose a threat.

Google Earth pictures show rows of Tornado aircraft and Chinook helicopters on the tarmac, with hardened bunkers nearby, while just inside what might have been the entrance to the base area, an elderly Phantom fighter plane is clearly visible, a memento of earlier times. I used Google Earth quite a bit to research the area. From it, I discovered that there is a train station, not too far away from the base. Though I could not quite make out all the perimeter fencing, I was pretty sure of where the entrance gate should be, and that I would be able to get a reasonable view of the base itself from the main road. Given the nature of the establishment, I resigned myself to going there, perhaps talking to the soldiers on the gate, taking some pictures and moving on. But a further bit of research raised my hopes just a little. There is a web site for the airbase, and among the listed staff was a Media and Public Relations officer. I noted the contact details, but decided against actually making contact until I had a reasonably accurate forecast of my possible visiting dates.

At first glance, the location of the base as a 'Coastal Station' is a little suspect. It appears to be nowhere near the coast! But in reality it is beside an estuary, and a little inland from the Royal and Ancient Golf Club at St. Andrews. In fact, the train station is given as 'Leuchars for St. Andrews'. Not too far away is Fife Ness itself, still the site of a coast guard station, and another former airbase. In thinking about the visit, I imagined that I may have more luck with the coastguards than with the RAF, so my initial planning involved them too. With a bit of luck, and help from yet another bike, it should be possible to visit both the RAF station and the coastguards from the Leuchars train station. Surely somebody would speak to me?

As spring turned into summer, and my all too busy diary had some decent gaps, the planning started to get much more definite. I had long since given up hope of the Grand Tour of all the remaining stations, but did harbour some remaining ideas of a 'Piccolo Tour', covering the remaining Scottish stations in a single round of the Scottish coast. Looking at timings, trains, ferries, and a possible bus journey the length of the Western Isles, from Stornoway to Castle Bay on Barra, it appeared just possible. But all too quickly that fatal phrase, "While I'm at it,...." took over. There are just too many good things to see and do on such a tour. How could a visit to Shetland ignore Orkney? And then Cape Wrath had always held a fascination, and that's not so far out of the way. Add in a few days on Coll on the way back from Tiree, and it looked like even a Piccolo tour could take all summer. Since the gaps in my diary did not stretch that far, more modest ambitions were in order, so I would have to be satisfied with a couple of bites at the Scottish coastal stations. The plans for two separate trips were almost settled, one up the east coast and the other up the west, when providence intervened. My travel companion of choice, Ginny, now my wife, (a status acquired since the coastal stations quest began) was recovering slowly from a foot operation, and cycling was not an option at this stage. I would have to be much less ambitious and look at travel that could be more easily sustained without too much leg work. The alternative of leaving her at home did not appeal. She had been endlessly encouraging of my quest, intrigued at first, doubtful of its possibility, but always supportive. More than once, she has waved me off at a station, or on the doorstep, smiling encouragement, with boundless belief in my ability to achieve what I set out to do. Her wish to be included in some of the travel was a further statement of support. Some small changes to my plans, to ensure her company was possible, seemed a small price to pay.

So the detailed planning shifted to Leuchars and Stornoway, since each was quite close to public transport, and could be comfortably reached even on wobbly feet! Fife Ness, and its coastguards, would have to be missed, not such a great loss to my quest since it has ceased to figure on the Shipping Forecast anyway. We would keep the wilder and more remote stations until later, when cycling would again become an option, and some of the possible side tours would be a welcome addition. By way of compensation, a shorter trip gave us the opportunity to meet up with friends now living in Scotland. Our route would virtually pass their doors.

The Google Earth picture of Leuchars showed just a short walk from the station to the entrance gate, and as I didn't imagine getting any further, this would not be too much of a challenge for Ginny. Since starting my quest, pleas with friends and family for

OS maps of each of the coastal station areas whenever the subject of birthday or Christmas presents came up had been heeded. So I could relate well what the satellite picture showed to my map. From the station, we would cross a busy road, walk alongside a housing estate, turn left for a few hundred meters and we would be at what I guessed was the entrance. How much time to allow? If we arrived at Leuchars station on one train, we could leave on the next, about an hour later, and still make good time to Inverness. A night there would be followed by a lunchtime bus to Ullapool, and so on to Stornoway. It looked perfect. A simple plan. Now I attempted to negotiate admission with the Media and Public Relations office, but this came to nothing. My emails elicited no reply, and several attempts to phone the number given were unanswered. However the website for RAF Leuchars advertised Air Display days which would take place around the time of our proposed visit. But the prospect of joining hoards of plane spotters and paying heavily for the privilege, on the off chance of getting to see some weather recording gear, lacked appeal. One final attempt to call the Public Relations Officer at last got an answer. A helpful lady answered and said she could arrange a visit provided I could put together a group of about 12, and booked a date many months ahead, oh, and there were no dates available until at least the following May. She was interested in my quest, listened sympathetically to my ideas, but suggested perhaps the best bet would be to try to join a college group, if there was a vacancy. I thanked her, but didn't see how this could help, so resigned myself to looking through the fence. At least the answer was clear.

Now the final planning got underway, train tickets and accommodation could be booked and we counted down to our departure once again. But we missed out on the customary early start for this trip, and so missed out the early morning Shipping Forecast with the current Weather Reports. Unaccountably, my usually early-wakening wife slept until the alarm went off, so was unable to wake me as she had often done in the past. But we did listen out for the normal Radio 4 forecast, which seemed excellent.

The one worry was the wind and rain that might arrive as we made our way back across The Minch from Stornoway. But timing the arrival of a rain band some days in advance is notoriously difficult, so there was a good chance it would come before, or after our crossing. In any case, going to Scotland and not having rain would be like going to the Sahara and getting wet. But come to think of it, my first visit to that desert had coincided with a deluge, so you never can tell.

While it was not exactly a leisurely start, we had time for breakfast before walking to the station, accompanied by increasing numbers of commuters as we neared our destination. It's been a while since either of us has taken a commuter train, and it was both reassuring and surprising that the streets were so busy, so early. The journey into London was uneventful, but when we descended to the Victoria Line at Vauxhall, we were reminded just how lucky we are not to make this journey daily. I joked that it seemed more crowded than Gatwick Airport, and though Ginny agreed, she pointed out that we needed to endure it for much less time than if we had been flying.

The East Coast mainline express train was ready as we arrived at King's Cross, so we boarded and quickly found our seats, window, table, facing the direction of travel. Perfect! And this time bought at a very reasonable price, on-line. The train was busy, but our travelling companions were well spaced out, though not beyond loud voice range. One young lady, travelling to Newcastle with her long suffering parents, kept up a verbal barrage the whole way. At times this was directed at them, at times into her phone, and at other times seemed targeted to enlighten the whole carriage. Turned out she was a drama teacher, clearly in rehearsal! Another passenger whiled away the miles playing with her mobile phone. When not talking on it, she was playing games, or texting. Pity she hadn't worked out how to turn off the key sounds. But these were minor intrusions on an otherwise great train journey.

Having travelled this way to Bridlington a couple of years previously, we should have remembered the remarkable feeling of speed demonstrated by our rapid progress beyond the M25, but somehow, we had forgotten. Before long we were well clear of London, unsure at first just how clear. Then we glimpsed a station, Hatfield, barely 20 minutes after setting off. Somewhere between here and our first stop at Doncaster, we checked the itinerary and realised that it was our wedding anniversary! We are not big celebrators of such things, so we laughed, exchanged a kiss and reminded each other that we had always planned adventures for our life together. The journey to Doncaster took just 2 hours, hardly time to savour the late summer countryside flashing by. But we did notice gradual changes as we sped north. Around London it seemed that all the crops had been harvested, and some fields even ploughed for the next sowing. With each passing hour, we noticed first combine harvesters at work in some fields, then fields of standing crops, brilliant in the late summer sunshine. It gave the look of a bumper harvest, and we smiled at the probable response of the farmers, "Oh, prices will be down again!" Distant relatives of mine are farmers, so we have many years of exposure to their woes.

Never having travelled this far northeast by train before, we were delighted by the many treasures revealed as we sped along. Durham, with its beautiful cathedral, for some reason started us thinking about Antony Gormley's renowned *Angel of the North*. We hardly had time to get out the map and check its location before I spotted it on the skyline, welcoming wings spread wide, just outside Newcastle. His installation of 100 cast iron figures at Crosby beach, *Another Place*, had attracted my attention on the way to the Isle of Man. Now here he was again. His works really have engaged people in a way not common for sculptors.

The train stopped at Newcastle for a few minutes for a crew changeover, then we were away again, rapidly closing on the Northumberland coast. More treasures came into view, beautiful Alnmouth, the station for Alnwick, then Bamburgh Castle, the

Farne Islands and Holy Island, its tidal causeway clear of the water
and busier than I imagined. Before long we had rounded Berwick-
on-Tweed and seamlessly crossed the border into Scotland. We
determined that Northumberland would repay another visit, and
further exploration at leisure.

Southern Scotland has its own delights. Soon after crossing the
border we were at the edge of the Southern Uplands, and again
closing on the coast, this time near St. Abbs Head, with its
lighthouse standing clear of the rocky coast. Not itself a coastal

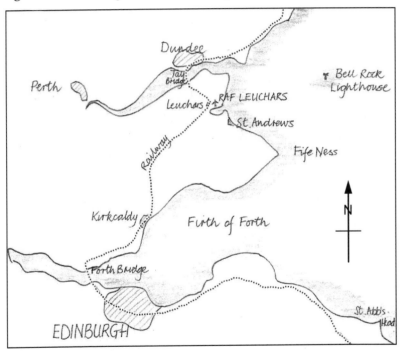

station, St. Abbs Head is one of the markers for the inshore
shipping forecast, which steps around the coast of Britain from one
famous headland to another. Perhaps that could be the seed of
some future quest.

Turning west, we had a good view across the wide Firth of Forth, to Fife Ness in the distance, the only view we could expect. The weather continued clear, and we drew into Edinburgh station in plenty of time to board our onward train, which would take us across the Firth of Forth and on to our destination, Leuchars!

Being a former railwayman, I was looking forward to crossing the Forth Bridge. There is something iconic about its design, something that shouts about the confidence of Victorian engineering. And of course it dates from just after the era of Fitzroy and the early forecasts. As we waited to change trains in Edinburgh beneath the castle and the rather too gothic Scott memorial, I recalled a story about the legendary painting of the Forth Bridge. My recollection was that a new highly durable coating had been applied to the Victorian steelwork some years ago, so that repainting would be unnecessary for 25 years or more. Thus would technology once again change the language, and the simile 'like painting the Forth Bridge' would no longer be meaningful. I looked forward to seeing the newly gleaming structure as we rounded the airport, and began our approach. But when we did, and the distinctive shape of the bridge came into view, there before us was a structure part shrouded in scaffolding and white plastic. It seems the application of the new long-life paint is taking rather longer than anticipated. Wouldn't it be ironic if the new paint takes so long to apply that it becomes a job, well, like painting the Forth Bridge?

Crossing the bridge did somehow symbolise an arrival. Suddenly, everything looked more distinctly Scottish. The houses couldn't be mistaken for English houses, the stations had their own character, and a look of recent renovation and upgrading. This was emphasised by the Gaelic spelling of station names alongside English, quite an innovation. Even the shape and size of the hills seemed distinctly Scottish, and when we caught sight of a blaze of purple heather, we felt we really had arrived.

Leuchars train station however is not in the hills, but in a broad sweep of the Fife coastal plain. Arriving felt a bit like déjà vu, since I had spent so much time looking at maps and satellite images. The airbase was clearly visible just across the main road as expected. And despite its purpose, the whole area looked very peaceful and calm in the afternoon sunshine.

We crossed the field to the perimeter of the airfield, vaguely expecting someone to shout at us. But even when I took out my binoculars, no challenge came. An RAF police car passed, without comment. Having failed to pick out anything that looked like a weather station from the end of the runway, we turned to walk to the main gate. The initial air of peace and calm was mildly disturbed by gaggles of children returning from school, but none of them turned to look as suddenly the air filled with menace as two Tornado fighters screamed low over the airfield and banked steeply, dodging a third fighter that appeared from nowhere. The three quickly disappeared from sight, the thunderous roar died away. Were they on an exercise, or responding to an action call? We will never know. The children are clearly used to such things, and probably used to seeing strangers duck and cover their heads too, because none of them laughed at us either.

Approaching the main gate, I looked for the Phantom so evident from the Google Earth pictures. Sure enough, there it was, but right beside it, on a similar stand, was a far from elderly Tornado. Seems the Google Earth picture has yet to catch up.

The usual welcome signs, and RAF badges adorned the gate area, but the armed guard on the gate looked anything but welcoming. From years of experience in Cyprus, Ginny cautioned me, practically begged me, not to take out my camera. But nothing suggested taking pictures was unwise, though I refrained, more because I was anxious to talk to the guards, than concern over whether or not I taking photos was permitted.

So I marched off purposefully to the door marked 'Guard Room', Ginny somewhat reluctantly following. Inside, we were met by a smartly dressed Corporal, who politely asked us to wait while he completed dealing with a delivery driver. Not surprisingly, they are reluctant to accept packages on behalf of others. In the corner of the room we spotted a cabinet containing a few souvenirs of the base on sale, and mused that it would be ironic if all we took away was a ball-point pen! Our turn came and we explained our mission. A sceptical look spread over the corporal's face when we outlined our proposals, but then he shook his head slowly, smiled and said "Well, I get lots of strange requests, but I've never heard one like this before!" He started thumbing through the base telephone directory, but without giving the impression that he had any idea what to look for. The situation was saved by the arrival of a lady, dressed in civilian clothes. The corporal started to explain what we were looking for, when she turned to us and asked if we were looking for the Met Office on site. Clearly she had a better knowledge of just what went on at the base than the corporal. But she too looked slightly quizzical when I explained some more. Could I speak to the Met Officer? What for? Well, I repeated the basis of the quest, and suggested that he might provide the current weather observations over the phone, for me at least a step closer to the actual coastal station.

A quick look in the phone book, a few numbers dialled and I was put on the phone to Alec, who said, yes, he was the person who prepared the hourly observations for onward transmission to the Met Office in Exeter and thence to the BBC. He was interested in the quest, and in what other stations we had visited. I asked for the current observations, and as he started to dictate them, he stopped and suggested that it would be easier if we came onto the base, and saw the weather station for ourselves. Bingo! He would speak to the Guard Room and then come to collect us at the gate in about 10 minutes, once he had completed the current observations and report. I looked at Ginny, who shook her head slowly and smiled. She had never doubted that we would be invited onto the base, though I had no such confidence. But clearly, spending time on the base would prevent our getting our booked train onward, with a couple of tight changes, to Inverness. We quickly agreed we could not pass up the opportunity to complete the visit for the sake of a railway timetable. There would be other trains, and it was still quite early.

With verbal approval from our civilian saviour, the corporal now cheerfully started preparing passes for us to visit the base, and asked if I had photographic ID. Perhaps I did have just a small hope of being admitted. Why else would I have been able to produce my Irish passport straight away? It was accepted without the bat of an eyelid. How different that would have been not many years ago. Just as the Soviet Union has disappeared as the external threat, so have the Irish ceased to be the threat they were seen as not so long ago. I have many memories of careful scrutiny of myself and my passport, and not a few intrusive questions at the UK borders in the past. Ginny had no ID, but it seems the Irish passport was good enough for both of us. Changed times indeed.

Having issued the passes, the corporal confessed himself keen to finish for the day. The sun was shining and the sky almost flawless blue. Being a motor bike fan, he was anxious to be out on the road, and enjoying the lately arrived summer. I mentioned that I had visited the Isle of Man weather station at Ronaldsway, and he became quite excited about his own visits to see the TT Races. We discussed the circuits, and the rather frightening crash barriers I had seen. He seemed unperturbed, and had even taken part in the 'open' events where members of the public are allowed to use the TT course in advance of the races. He discussed speeds which I imagined only possible on French Railways. As a member of the RAF Regiment, he had completed tours of duty in the Gulf, Iraq and Afghanistan. Not really surprisingly, he thought the Isle of Man TT races more scary than these tours of duty overseas. It seems his wife agreed, and wanted him to pack up the motor biking but not the RAF.

With the 4 pm weather report complete, Alec arrived at the guard post soon afterwards, and we climbed into his car for the short journey across the base. The soldier at the gate waved us through with a rather cursory look at our newly issued passes, and we passed under the nose of the Phantom and between the hangars to the edge of the runway. Not having any military knowledge, nor any real inclination to acquire any, I could make little sense of the various bits and pieces lying about. No doubt the hangars contained formidable bits of military hardware, but everything was screened from our view.

We arrived at the Met Office car park, and Alec guided us towards a low building at the edge of a taxiway, the former control tower for the base. Off to one side was the enclosure with the now familiar collection of weather recording instruments. There was no objection to taking pictures, but not that much to take pictures of! We went inside, to the main weather reporting and recording room. A familiar and rather anonymous bank of computer screens were stacked up on the desks, but on top of one was a rather welcome, and clearly loved barograph, of which more later. Alec introduced us to his colleague, Bob, who immediately endeared himself to Ginny by uttering the magic words, "Would you like a cup of tea?" Welcome words indeed after a long day's journey. As the tea brewed, Alec and Bob showed us some of their equipment, and we started to discuss the discernability or otherwise of climate change. Bob showed us some graphical representations of temperature, and also rainfall over the last ten years or so. In truth, it was impossible to see any obvious pattern, perhaps the odd spike here and there, but no overall change. We speculated that this may in fact be the pattern, that overall there is in fact little change, but there are clearly more extreme events, while in the background the overall change is barely discernable in the short run, but over a longer period will exert itself. Always there is the problem of distinguishing between variations in the weather, and a longer term, relentless slow change that will have its real impact decades from now. How much effect can we really have on this longer term change? It remains to be seen, probably when our grandchildren reach our sort of age.

Talk of extreme events brought us back to the present, and we discussed how much difficulty automated equipment has in picking up local, and sometimes violent, events. For example, Alec had seen thunderstorms approach, deluge the town, but miss the airfield, so no record of them would appear on their reports, if they were entirely automated. This was a recognised problem with automated recording, which I heard from most weather observers. Being an airfield, visibility is very important, but again, automated equipment usually just measures the degree of opaqueness between two sensors a metre or so apart. Thus the valley can be hidden in low-lying fog, but if the instruments are above it, they may show excellent visibility. Fog banks are hard for automatic instruments to detect, but of course are obvious to an observer.

To illustrate this, Alec pointed to the barograph on top of the desk. Its advantage for the observers, he explained, was that during extreme events, for example a thunderstorm, pressure changes occurred very rapidly. These are recorded by the automatic sensors at intervals, but the changing numbers are less obvious than the dropping needle. Alec explained how at an RAF station in Germany where he had been posted, he had witnessed a particularly severe thunderstorm approach and leave rapidly. So rapidly had the pressure changed that it had sucked water from the drains around the airfield. How do you record an event like that on a weather report? But the barograph recorded the event faithfully as an ink line across the graph paper, giving a much better picture of the pressure changes than the numbers recorded by the sensors. Come to think of it, after an initial fascination with digital watches, most people went back to the traditional analogue displays. It seems that the picture of time given a 'clock' display is more easily assimilated than the numbers. So it appears with pressure recording.

As if to emphasise this point, the large clock on the wall was an analogue clock, and catching a glimpse of it at first had me checking my own watch. But I quickly realised it was set on GMT, or Universal Co-ordinated Time (UTC)[1] as it is now more properly called.

Alec had many stories to tell. He has been a weather observer for many years, and seems to have chosen some interesting postings when the opportunities arose. He described working in the Falkland Islands, where he had an eighteen month posting. It seems quite a lonely place, but clearly rewarding. Later he worked at the Met Office headquarters when it was in Bracknell, but he didn't wish to make the move to Exeter, so opted for a posting back in Scotland, first in Eskdale Muir, then his current location.

Since he knew so many of the weather stations, I asked about the demise of Fife Ness as a reporting coastal station. While he was not entirely clear about the reasons, it seemed to be connected with the financial arrangements between the Maritime and Coast Guard Agency and the Met Office. He still receives weather reports from Fife Ness at Leuchars and forwards them to the Met Office, along with other reports. In fact there are many automatic stations around the coast which quietly report directly to the Met Office, and are not mentioned on any news bulletin. Often the details are available on some web site or other, just for the asking. The Met Office itself makes some information freely available, but charges for other details. It's odd to see observations that the Met Office would like to charge for freely available, for example, on the US National Oceanic and Atmospheric Administration web site[2]. Search the Met Office for observations from Fife Ness, and you will find nothing, but search the NOAA web site, and not only can you find Fife Ness, but also nearby Bell Rock lighthouse on the infamous Inchcape Rock.

In fact, Bell Rock was the local reporting station until 1984, when Fife Ness took over. Probably all the lighthouses report weather, automatically now since they are all thankfully unmanned.

Perhaps lighthouse keeping sounded romantic at one time, but try to imagine life for three months at a time somewhere like Bell Rock. Such postings always came with a serious risk, not just the possibility of the relief boat being delayed. In December 1955, a helicopter crew on a training flight from Leuchars decided to drop a package of mail and newspapers to the Bell Rock crew stranded in the awful weather. Something went tragically wrong, and the helicopter's rotor touched the roof of the lighthouse, damaged the light but missed the waiting lighthouse keepers before crashing onto the rocks below. The lighthouse keepers made a heroic but fruitless attempt to rescue a crewman they could see in the wrecked cockpit, but he was already dead. Almost immediately afterwards, the huge waves carried away what was left of the wreck. Despite the trauma for all concerned, it appears that another helicopter crew from Leuchars delivered a festive dinner to the Bell Rock on Christmas day. Health and Safety assessments must have been done differently in those days.

Both Alec and Bob were very interested in our quest, and in our immediate plans to travel on to Stornoway. We discussed the stations already visited, and those still to come, the hospitality of the observers and the special nature of each station. Bob called up a detailed forecast for our journey to and from the Hebrides. It appeared we would be in luck on the journey out, since the wind would be light, and any showers soon clearing. But following some overnight wind and rain, we could expect a wet and possibly uncomfortable trip back across the Minch, much the same as we determined earlier. We discussed our planned visit to Lerwick, possibly during the winter, and Alec confirmed that it was still staffed, and probably will remain so, since they launch weather balloons, the only other one still to do so, with Valentia. Other stations are gradually being converted to automatic operation, but Leuchars too will probably retain its status as there are always special requirements for the RAF that can only really be met by having staff on site.

By now it was time for the next hourly observation to be made and reported, so we accompanied Alec outside to check on the visibility and cloud cover. Back in the office, the automatic readings had been prepared by the instruments and were there on the computer screen. Alec had the opportunity to review and accept or modify as appropriate, then add in his own observations before pressing the button to send this weather report from RAF Leuchars to the Met Office.

That report neatly rounded off our visit, and Alec very kindly offered to drop us at the station to join the next train onward to Dundee, to continue our journey. We had booked places on trains for our journey all the way through to Inverness, but clearly we had now missed out on these bookings. As the train arrived in Leuchars station, I mused on the possibility that our tickets would not be valid on our revised schedule, but reasoned that the visit we had just accomplished was more than compensation for possibly having to pay for a new ticket.

Still in bright sunshine, we settled down for the short journey across the Firth of Tay to Dundee and a change of trains. Now all railwaymen, and many with no railway connections, know of the Tay Bridge disaster, when the first Tay Bridge collapsed as a train crossed it during a violent storm on 28 December 1879. Seventy five people, all those on board the train, died in the disaster. The enquiry found many faults, in both the design and the building of the bridge, and thus contributed to safer designs for the future. A new bridge was duly built and survives to this day. But somewhere in the back of my mind, I seemed to remember that the foundations of the original bridge are still visible alongside the current bridge. I was on the lookout for these when the bridge turned east as it reached the north shore of the Firth. This gave a splendid view back along the length of the bridge, and there sure enough were the stumps of the original pillars visible well above the water, alongside the pillars supporting the bridge. Later, I checked an image on Google Earth, and was pleasantly surprised to find they are clearly visible, though if you didn't know what you were looking for, you might find the picture unremarkable.

We joined our next train at Dundee, where the guard explained politely that our tickets were not valid, but quickly added that she would accept them. She enquired as to why we had missed our booked train, and whether or not it was the fault of the railway company. We could only say that it was entirely our own fault, having been detained at Leuchars longer than we had expected. She explained that our discounted ticket was not really valid, since it was now the rush hour, though there was space enough. On the short trip to Perth, to make another connection, she was happy to 'overlook' this, but suggested that we may have a problem moving on from Perth. Our best option, she explained, was to approach the guard before joining the train and to explain the situation.

Thus warned, we arrived in Perth and with nearly an hour to wait, decided to find a meal before moving on. The station cafe was welcoming, but basic. A rather uninspiring menu was displayed on a chalk board, but as we tried to make a choice between indifferences, the assistant appeared and informed us in an apologetic voice that the kitchen was now closed. We must have appeared hungry, and disappointed, as he then brightened and offered to toast some panini for us, from a small but acceptable range. We made our choice, and then quickly opted for a couple of glasses of wine to supplement our simple feast. All in all, it seemed a small celebration was in order. All our travel arrangements had worked well in the end, and we had succeeded in getting into an RAF base!

Fed and watered, if not quite in the manner we had hoped, we found the platform for our onward journey to Inverness. Perth is a large and windswept station, obviously less busy now than in former times. There seemed to be far too much space, and too many derelict buildings just beyond the platforms, and a vast web of tracks just outside the station. Our train duly appeared, negotiated the maze of points and drew into the platform. Forewarned, we approached the guard, who seemed to be taking instructions from another staff member, and dealing with other passengers too.  Was this where things would start to go wrong? But we explained the situation, showed our tickets, with the expired reservations and were not surprised when the guard said, no, they were invalid, and we would need new ones.  He told us to board the train, and he would arrange things when we were underway.  But when we had seated ourselves, and the journey got underway, he arrived at our seats, asked for the tickets, then gave us a big smile and said he would let us off this time, though strictly speaking etc. etc.  It seems that privatisation or not, train staff are not always so stone hearted as we read.

The line from Perth to Inverness is probably a delight at any time of the year, but in late summer it all looked particularly so.  We climbed slowly up the Tay valley, crisscrossing the river and occasionally the road.  By volume, the Tay is the biggest river in the British Isles, apparently discharging more water into the North Sea than the Severn does into the Irish Sea.  I suppose this just confirms that Scotland is even wetter than Wales!  But in the late evening sun, it all seemed delightful, with no sign of rain, though there was plenty of water in the river.  Agriculture and woodland covered the wide valley floor, with the hills beyond just showing a hint of purple.  Beyond Dunkeld, the river splits, then after Pitlochry the valley narrows and the real mountains begin.  Soon we were climbing up through Glen Garry, beyond the trees, and out across marshlands, with sheep and the occasional deer picking their way across the landscape.

I suppose you could say the high point of the journey was Pass of Drumochter, for not only does it have magnificent mountain vistas in all directions, but it is in fact the highest point on the UK railway network, acknowledged by a rather weather battered sign, proclaiming us to be 462 metres above sea level.  Now we watched the marshlands gradually yield to streams flowing north.  In turn these combined to another significant river, and before long we were descending the Spey Valley, skirting the massive Cairngorm Mountains. We stopped briefly at Aviemore, with its 'ski village in summer' look, and the coaches for the steam railway lined up waiting for the weekend.

By now it was beginning to get dark, well, at least dusk, the long drawn out dusk of Scotland in summer, as the train descended to Inverness, taking a long loop east, then west to cope with the step gradient out of the hills. Journey's end for the day, a long day but a rewarding one was not far away. But.... increasingly tired after our long day travelling, we arrived at our hotel, the Royal Highland Hotel, right by the station, and claimed our room. Horror! The only room available was a smoking room! This despite my clear instructions and the hotel's confirmation. Now this may seem a small inconvenience, but with the increasing policy of making hotel rooms non-smoking, any room offered as 'smoking' can be guaranteed to smell horrible, and would certainly give me a headache. I demanded a room be found, at another hotel if necessary. With a smile, and very good grace, the receptionist not only found us a hotel, but also a taxi to take us there, all at the Royal Highland's expense. Full marks for sorting a customer's problems. We could have done without the delay, and the aggravation, but nevertheless were glad to fall into bed, and prepare for our next adventure in the morning, over the sea to Stornoway!

---

[1] Just why Universal Coordinated Time should be abbreviates at UTC I cannot say. For a discussion on UTC and GMT see
en.wikipedia.org/wiki/Coordinated_Universal_Time.

[2] www.noaa.gov.

# Stornoway

58 ° 13′ N      6° 19′ W

South southwest 3, 25 miles, Fair, 1004, Falling

August 2009

The trip to Stornoway was planned as a follow on from the Leuchars visit, though it had not originally been so. However, with Ginny's limited mobility, it now made good practical sense. Neither Leuchars nor Stornoway weather stations were too far from public transport, and a convenient train and bus journey linked them. The problem is though, when I come to write about it, where do I begin? Leaving Leuchars? Arriving at Inverness? Or leaving Inverness? It's difficult to say just where it actually began; the choice of the morning after, in Inverness is arbitrary.

Having been found a non-smoking room, late at night, we had little inclination to do anything other than fall into bed and sleep. But in the morning, we had more time to reflect. The Beaufort Hotel, into which we had been transferred by the Royal Highland, was comfortable and welcoming. The name immediately caught my eye, but there was nothing to suggest a connection with the Admiral, a patron of Robert Fitzroy throughout his career. In fact, Admiral Beaufort had been instrumental in the temporary appointment of Fitzroy to command the *Beagle* on her first voyage to South America. He had then sponsored Fitzroy for *Beagle's* second voyage, and sanctioned the inclusion of 'a suitable gentleman companion' for the voyage. This of course was Charles Darwin. Beaufort himself was a major contributor to science and cartography, and later again was instrumental in Fitzroy's appointment by the Admiralty to establish a Metrological Office. Beaufort is the man who established the commonly used wind scale and for whom it is named. So when the Shipping Forecast talks of 'Severe Gale 9', it is referring to force 9 on the Beaufort Scale[1] which rates the relative strengths of wind, in a similar way that the Richter Scale rates the relative strengths of earthquakes.

Clearly the only room that had been available in the Beaufort Hotel was a honeymoon suite as both the bed and the bathroom were huge. The latter had a spa bath with ceiling star lights, and dimmers. Pity we had no time to use it all. For us, the hotel having passed the first test and delivered a comfortable non-smoking room, the next test of excellence was breakfast. This test too the Beaufort passed with flying colours. On the menu, both kippers and porridge! Now that's a real Scottish breakfast to get us ready to be on our way, and to keep off the drizzle which was now visible outside.

After breakfast we made enquiries about the name of the hotel but these met with blank looks. It seemed the manager, reasonably new to the post, had no idea, either of the origin of the name, nor of the famous associations with it. But a quick look on the internet shows the Admiral as really the only reference of any note; and far from having a Scottish connection, he was from Ireland, though descended from a Huguenot family. We mused on the possibility that the hotel could use this information as a sales pitch, maybe naming the dining room 'The Admiral' Cabin', or the bar 'The Gale Force Bar'.

There are various ways of reaching Stornoway and the Western Isles, or Na h-Eileanan Siar to give them their official and correct name in Gaelic. The obvious route is to go to Ullapool, from where the ferry crosses The Minch directly to Stornoway. But Na h-Eileanan Siar are very special islands, a string of cultural pearls on the remote edge of Europe, so unique that such a direct approach could seem inappropriate. Their isolation and history have preserved something of a way of life unique in itself, and long absent from the mainland of Scotland. Dipping into Stornoway and out again would give us no chance to savour these special charms. But mobility dictated a short visit. My earlier plans had included the possibility of travelling the length of the island chain, by bus and ferry. Such a trip would have included the weather station on Tiree, then Barra, South Uist, Benbecula, North Uist and Harris before finally arriving on Lewis, and so to Stornoway. But that was not to be. We would have to be content with the short visit.

Fortunately, we had made a more extended visit to the Isles some years ago, and so would carry the flavours we acquired then with us on this visit. On that trip, equipped with bicycles, Ginny and I had flown from Glasgow in a little plane, touched down briefly on Tiree, and continued to Barra, where the runway is the beach. This is unique in Europe, perhaps in the world, a regular air service depending on the times of the tides as well as the state of the weather. Unloading bicycles from a plane on a beach, then cycling off to explore the islands gave us a great thrill, the feeling of starting a real expedition. There are many wonderful and unique things to explore, if you visit at leisure, amongst them the continuing use of Gaelic.

Gaelic culture is strong in the Isles, but in case you imagine it to be the remnant of Scottish culture from before the Union and the Clearances, in truth it is the result of an earlier colonial enterprise. The Gaelic of the Isles is similar to Irish Gaelic because the whole of the west of Scotland was colonised by Irish chieftains, whose settlements displaced the earlier Pictish culture. From the Isles, the Irish Chiefs gradually extended their political and cultural power over much of the north of Scotland, and retained their influence, as the Lords of the Isles, until quite recent times. My own schooling in Ireland had covered these events, but they are quite unknown in much of Scotland, never mind England. And my own knowledge of Irish Gaelic helps to read the Scottish signs and to decode names on the map, but the pronunciation is so different between the two that conversation had proved impossible on our earlier visit. On that visit we had imbibed something of the special magic of the Isles, cycling from Barra in the south up through the Uists and Benbecula to Harris, the southern and more mountainous part of the main island. But we had not had time to continue to Lewis and Stornoway, so took the ferry to Skye and cycled back through the island to Kyle of Lochalsh and then home by train. Lewis itself always appealed as a destination to explore, and still does. Unfortunately, on this visit we would have no opportunity to see anything outside Stornoway.

There are aspects of the Island culture that are considerably less attractive. The southern islands are Catholic, the northern ones fundamentalist Presbyterian. Until just before our visit, they did not allow the ferry between Ullapool and Stornoway to operate on Sundays, a situation which the ferry company, CalMac, changed on the rather dubious pretence that human rights may have been involved. Binge drinking is a major social issue in the north. From our vantage point on bicycles, we noticed that the road sides are littered with small empty whisky bottles, the contents drunk in the privacy of a car, and then discarded away from the neighbours' eyes. The effects are all too apparent in the emergency admissions to Stornoway hospital at the weekends.

The buses from Inverness to Ullapool are timed to connect with the ferry, so before leaving we had the whole morning to explore the town. The obvious starting point, well obvious to us at any rate, was to take a look at the Caledonian Canal. This is another piece of Victorian engineering dating from Fitzroy's time. The chief engineer responsible was none other than Thomas Telford. The structure was designed to enable warships to pass between the North Sea and the West without making the dangerous passage around Cape Wrath. As a consequence the locks are very large, much larger than normal on British canals. However, the canal was not long completed when warship design, iron construction and steam propulsion made it somewhat redundant. The newer ships were simply too large to pass through the locks, big as they were. Now its chief benefit is for tourist related activity, though there are occasional passages by smaller commercial and navy vessels.

To get to the canal, we crossed the Greig Street pedestrian bridge, a suspension bridge built in 1881 across the river Ness. This is a delightful structure, all white lattice work against the dark river. An additional delight is the way it resonates as people walk across it, not quite enough to make pedestrians seasick, but disconcerting nonetheless. However, when you think about London's wobbly bridge and remember this has been in place for over a hundred and twenty years, you do wonder what the fuss was about.

We knew we were getting close to the canal when we saw yacht masts way above the houses on either side of the road. Right enough, our path led us to the middle of the flight of locks that take boats from sea level to the first significant section of the canal. Two yachts were in the second lock, their crews waiting patiently as the water lifted them towards their goal. Approaching the yachts, one of the crew caught my eye, and we looked at each other in astonishment. He and I had been shipmates aboard the tallship *Soren Larsen* sailing in the Pacific, and had last seen each other on the dock at Lautoka, Fiji, some eighteen months previously. We had a little time to catch up on news of mutual acquaintances and the ship herself as the lock filled. The news of the latter was not good. Leaving New Zealand as winter approached, for another Pacific voyage, she had been struck by a rogue wave which severely damaged the ship. Fortunately, with superb seamanship and help from the coast guard, she made it back to land safely, with no loss of life, but a huge bill for repair and the loss of the whole season's voyage. But our reminiscences drew to a close once the lock was full and the yachts made ready to depart, so we said our goodbyes once again, and went our separate ways.

Ginny and I returned to the town centre for a quick bite to eat in the Victoria Market. This was once a meat and vegetable market, but now caters largely for the tourist and luxury trade. But there are a couple of shops selling fish and meat still, if a rather refined version of their former selves. Game birds and venison seemed to be the fare of choice. But at least there is good coffee and tasty, if expensive, sandwiches on offer. Though the mouth of the river Ness is an obvious place for a town, Inverness is relatively new, having been laid out by the English as a fortress town following the defeat of the Jacobites at nearby Culloden. So its streets follow a grid pattern, unusual in older towns, though used extensively by the Romans. In fact, the site has been inhabited since prehistoric times, but the Romans never came this far north, and towns were never developed by the Celts. Any attempt by the Sassenach, (as the English are called in Scots and Irish Gaelic), to suppress Scottish culture clearly failed. We saw many kilts worn in and around the town, and not just by a fashion conscious elite. Many clearly ordinary folk seemed to wear the tartan as a matter of course. Just how practical it is in wet and windy weather, I remain to be convinced.

By now, readers will be aware that language usage and variation is a theme of these travels, particularly where different languages meet and interact, as in Scotland and Ireland. So moving to the bus station to look for our transport to Ullapool, we came across another use of words to intrigue and delight. It's always amusing when seemingly very different words are used for familiar things. In India I was quickly aware that asking for directions to the 'bus station' resulted in very puzzled looks. Trains leave from stations, buses from bus stands. Here in Inverness, there is a bus station, but the individual boarding points are bus 'stances'. Now where does that come from? Still, we found the correct stance, and our coach, which waited a little while after its due departure time for a connecting service from Aberdeen.

Perhaps it was a general dampness in the air that persuaded the bus driver to turn the heating up full, because as we crossed the Black Isle on our way north, the temperature in the bus rose and rose.   But the scenery compensated for any discomfort, first agricultural then, as we turned inland, a wilder and wilder landscape until we pulled out of the valley onto the Scottish moors. But this is far from a real wilderness, as it soon became clear that the whole area is extensively developed for hydro-electricity.   A wide dam loomed on the horizon, and channels and pipes crossed the area, collecting and funnelling the water to deliver 'green' energy.   I'm not so sure that we would be willing to accept this level of intrusion into a remote area nowadays, even in the face of climate change and the need to increase the production of renewable energy.   However, the industrial heritage aspects of such schemes are not without their own beauty.

It didn't seem such a long time, discounting the ridiculous heat on the bus, before we left the hydro-electric lakes behind, and began a very pleasant descent through an increasingly wooded valley towards Loch Broom, the sea loch on which Ullapool stands.   The views became more expansive, with rugged mountains, purple clad, rising out of the calm water on either side of the loch.   Before long, the town of Ullapool itself came into view, a pleasing line of white houses, peat fires smoking, stretching along the water's edge, towards the quay.   But where was the ferry?   Since the bus was timed to meet up with the Stornoway ferry, we had expected it to be there.   Perhaps our assurance of reasonable weather had been unfounded, and the ferry was struggling across The Minch?

However, a quick check at the booking office revealed nothing more dramatic than a delay due to 'operating difficulties', and a scheduled departure some 45 minutes late.   Meantime, we had the opportunity to stretch our legs with a walk out to the end of the harbour.   Disconcertingly in such a pristine loch, with clear waters and clean air, a sign warned 'Danger, Sewage Outfall'.   But from a safe distance, we stood and watched as the ferry appeared from amongst the islands and slowly hove into the harbour. The sight could have been used for a travel poster for Scotland, purple hillside, hazy blue sky, dark calm water with a traditionally coloured ferry making speed to the terminal.

Quite quickly the arriving cars and passengers disembarked and we made our way aboard, and up to the top deck to enjoy the view and the weak afternoon sunshine. Soon we were on our way again, past the sewage outfall, beneath the heather-clad slopes and out amongst the islands. Very much to our surprise we were quickly inspected by a small pod of dolphins which sped toward the ship, leaping and swimming quite close to the sides. But just as quickly as they had arrived, they were gone, though we kept peering at the waves, almost urging them to reappear. Other wildlife stayed close by, gulls and skuas, gannets and kittiwakes were all around, making the most of the long daylight hours to feed their chicks, traces of which were clearly visible on the island cliffs. Further out to sea we looked back on the receding mainland, a lumpy collection of mountains with forbidding flanks shelving to the sea. Sutherland stretches north from here, a wild and remote coast named by the Vikings for whom it was a southern land.

Out to the west, the even more remote Shiant Islands came into view. Formed by a volcanic intrusion, they are very difficult to visit, though I did manage to spend a night at anchor there some years ago, and go ashore and wonder just how anyone ever managed to eek out a living there. We could also distinguish a vaguely familiar sight to the south where the mountains of Skye reared up from the sea. Returning from the bike trip I mentioned at the start of the chapter, we crossed Skye from Uig to Portree by way of the dramatic descent through the mountains now clearly visible. Completing a dramatic pictorial panorama, surprisingly soon the peaks of southern Lewis emerged from the evening mist, quickly followed by the lower elevations of northern Lewis delineated from the Atlantic by the Butt of Lewis headland. With the help of a map and a compass, we were able to identify many of the headlands and lighthouses distinctly visibly in the still comfortable late evening sunshine.

But our eyes kept turning west, to try to identify the features now emerging as Stornoway crept slowly into view. Gradually we passed Chicken Head on the Eye Peninsula then in towards the mouth of Stornoway harbour, with its calm water, surprisingly busy and spacious. We kept our eyes peeled for signs of the airport, with its weather station, but saw nothing of it. However, by way of a welcome to this beautiful place, a soft rain started to fall, driving us below for the last minutes of the voyage. Alongside the ferry berth, a French expedition cruise ship, *Le Diamant*, was taking its complement of Zodiac inflatable boats back aboard, while another pocket sized cruise ship, the *National Geographic Explorer* was anchored out further in the harbour. These glorious islands may not seem to be the obvious places to go cruising, but unless weather is your over riding criterion, who could argue that they have, in fact, as much to offer as the more obvious destinations for cruise ships? Thankfully for the locals, the huge cruise ships that dominate harbours in the Aegean and the Caribbean have so far kept away.

European Community money has built much of the infrastructure in the remote parts of Europe, and here is no exception. We landed at a smart new ferry terminal, protected from the rain. Outside, a large wooden copy of one of the Lewis Chessmen stood guard over the entrance, a charming reference to the rich cultural heritage of these islands. Unfortunately little is known of their history before their discovery in 1831, wrapped in cloth on the west coast of Lewis[2]. I had thought they were a set, but there are some 93 pieces in all, the remains of several sets, just how many is unclear. They were probably carved in Norway, mostly from walrus ivory, though a few are made from whale teeth. As most of them are currently in the British Museum in London, I hope to have the opportunity to see them for real in the future. The rest are in Edinburgh. This is a cause of friction, with nationalist opinion wanting them all moved to Edinburgh, though in fact Lewis itself may be a more suitable place for them, while Norway has yet to lodge a claim.

We left the ferry terminal in continuing steady rain, and quickly found our hotel, the Caladh Inn, a rather municipal looking building just a short walk from the quay. The welcome was friendly though inspection of our tiny room revealed the municipal exterior concealed an even more austere interior. The bathroom was straight out of a 1950s council house, functional, clean, but of terrible design.

The dining room had a similar time warp feel about it, offering a carvery menu, for breakfast, lunch and dinner, all at different prices. However, the staff shattered any feeling of isolation. As I had found elsewhere on my travels in Ireland and UK, hotel and catering workers now come largely from outside the area, from Eastern Europe in particular. It's rare to find locals in these positions.

The night was windy and rainy, as forecast by our friends in RAF Leuchars, but by the morning the rain had stopped, leaving low cloud over the town. Back in the dining room, it became clear that municipal or not, the hotel was a staging post for coach tours of the islands. Large party groups tucked into standard breakfast buffet fare. No chance of kippers here, but the porridge was good. The real test though is always the coffee. I chose tea, Ginny coffee and again I won! Never mind, we were sufficiently fortified to set out for our walk to the airport.

The rain had stopped, but in its place we now had a cloud of midges to cope with as we walked through the early morning town. Our first destination was the rather prominent coastguard building we had seen from the ferry as we entered the harbour. I knew the actual weather station was automatic, so I thought talking to the coastguards might be the only way to find out any information about it from a live source. Not for the first time, when we arrived at an official station, we were welcomed almost as if we were expected. A mention of the weather drew a warm and knowing smile from the lady at reception. "You'll want to meet Angus," she said and led us into the back of the building and upstairs. In a large office, with banks of computer screens all around, we met Angus, who gave us a brief introduction to the work undertaken by the Stornoway coastguards. The area they are responsible for is very large, covering not just the Western Isles, but

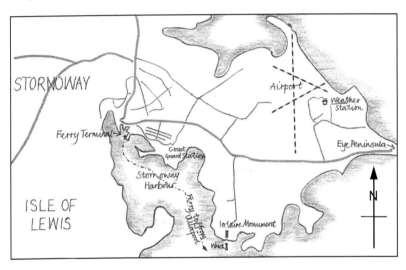

parts of the Scottish mainland coast too. Any emergency in this area is likely to involve this control centre, and indeed we had heard on the morning news of the recovery of a climber's body from the Cullins by helicopter the previous day. Sadly, there is a steady though irregular stream of casualties to be dealt with. As regards the weather reporting, Angus confirmed that the station is at the airport and that it has been automatic for 4 or 5 years. His own role in the weather is to be the voice that is heard on the radio and on the coastguard VHF transmissions. And a very fine and clear voice it is too! The local forecast, though, is received from the Met Office at Exeter, and none of it is generated by the coastguards themselves.

With this information, we said our good-byes and set off again to walk to the airport. There are buses, but we were in no hurry, and the distance is quite short, so we enjoyed the chance to stretch our legs after the long journeys of the previous two days. Our journey took us along the seashore, then out to the road where we saw an example of local adaptation to climate. Lacking trees, the birds of the Western Isles are always on the lookout for suitable nesting sites. Post-boxes, particularly in remote locations, are highly favoured by robins, so the Post Office has fitted little shutters over the letter-openings to avoid interruptions to service, or to incubation.

We passed the end of the runway, complete with scare-crows, and turned down the access road. At the entrance to the airport itself we found a little memorial to the RAF, which established the airfield during the war for anti-submarine patrols and coastal defence. In fact, there are many buildings, some abandoned, that seem to date from those times. But further on, a very modern building came into view, the Airport Terminal.

We scanned the area for the telltale signs of a weather station. Beside the runway, we could see a mast with some instruments, but this looked more like a local observation point. Behind the terminal building, however, on a small hill, we could distinguish a high fenced enclosure which seemed to bristle with masts and boxes. Surely that was what we were looking for? How could we check before making the climb, and perhaps triggering a security alert? The only possible source of information would be the airport information desk inside the terminal, so that's where we went.

Entering the terminal was like entering a different and unfamiliar world; suddenly we felt almost intimidated! But we quickly warmed to the prospect of a decent coffee and a chance to sit down in comfortable surroundings. Refreshed, we watched travellers hurrying back and forth. Something about a small airport terminal is very appealing. What crowds there are, are very small. It seemed that many travellers knew each other, and all were accompanied by friends and relatives to the departure gate. Each plane on the tarmac was small, and their load was correspondingly small. Time was when all air travel was on such a small scale. And in truth we are old enough to remember those times.

When things cleared a little, we approached the lady at the information desk. Explaining what we were looking for drew a smile, and head shake. She had no knowledge of the weather station, but as we explained our mission a little further, her face brightened, and she asked us to wait a moment while she phoned a friend, PJ. She had a few words with him, and then handed the phone to me. PJ turned out to be the met officer for the airport, and had worked for the Met Office at the weather station until it was automated. Not wishing to leave Stornoway, he had 'jumped the fence', along with some others, and now worked directly for the airport. As is the case at Leuchars, pilots need local and current weather observations to operate safely, so many airports employ their own met officers to provide it. PJ confirmed the location of the now automatic weather station, on the hill where we had surmised. He also told us that just behind the terminal were the buildings which housed the staff when the station had been manned. PJ could not really supply much more information. He suggested we go to the enclosure, take a look, but no one around had a key. Nor was there anyone around to ask more about the automatic station. We thanked our informant, and left the terminal building to take a look.

We followed the small path up to the wire enclosure, with its secure fence and well padlocked gate. We took guesses as to which of the instruments were which, but some were just large metal boxes, indistinguishable from one another to the lay person. No sign here of a barograph, nor a recognisable thermometer! Not even a clock was readable from the perimeter fence. However, we were still satisfied to have reached our goal! We took the inevitable pictures of each other, but looking at them now, they hardly capture the excitement we both felt. We are each bundled up against a grey day, while the tiny airport in the background looks like some kind of model.

Now there was little left to do but to have a look at the former office, and thank the lady at information, before taking a taxi back to Stornoway. We had a couple of hours before the ferry was due to leave, so we asked the driver to take us to the centre of Stornoway. On the way, we had a little time to talk to the driver about his life in Lewis. I asked was he local, 'No!' came the reply, but from 'An Rubha', the Eye Peninsula, a few miles east from the airport. I suppose there's local and there's local. But he had travelled, as a seaman, like so many of his compatriots. I tried to establish whether or not they spoke Gaelic at home, explaining my Irish origins. At first he seemed to suggest they did, but later he seemed to suggest otherwise. On his travels, he had met many Irish people though, and with one in particular he remembered sharing conversation in Gaelic. We tried out a few words with each other, and found many similarities but quickly lost the thread, with our very different pronunciations.

On our way back into Stornoway we passed a very new Tesco. Like most of the signs we had seen around the town, its major signs were in Gaelic and English, but with the Gaelic given prominence. Interesting to see how a national chain can adapt to make itself look local.

After a coffee in town, we visited the tourist office, chiefly to get some postcards to send to others of my friends who had previously been part of my quest. Reproductions of the Lewis chessmen abound, just as we had seen Loch Ness Monsters aplenty in Inverness.

But what really caught our attention at the information office were various books referring to a WW 1 era disaster at Stornoway. Further examination revealed the full horror of the wreck of the *Iolaire*. It made tragic reading.

On January 1st 1919, the motor yacht *Iolaire* was bringing soldiers and seamen back to Stornoway from their war service. For reasons never explained, the ship hit rocks at the very mouth of the harbour in the middle of the night. The final death toll was officially put at 205, of whom 181 were islanders, but the ship was badly overcrowded, as men struggled to get home from the front, so the death toll could have been higher. A local Lewis man saved 40 people, swimming ashore with a heaving line, along which many of the survivors made their way to safety. Only 75 passengers survived the disaster. The soldiers and sailors were wearing their full uniforms including heavy boots, so swimming from the wreck would have been difficult, though in fact most men of that time had never learned to swim.

The inconclusive findings of the Admiralty enquiry generated considerable ill-feeling amongst the Lewis population. Drunkenness among the crew was discounted, but might have been a factor, though the ship was sailing at night in poor visibility into a difficult harbour entrance.

The loss of such a large number of men from such a small community and so close to home, after years of service abroad must have been shattering indeed for the whole population. Few villages escaped the tragedy. There is a rather poignant memorial just down the road from the coastguard station, above the site of the wreck. A little way away from the shore, a navigation beacon now marks the dangerous rocks on which *Iolaire* foundered.

With this tragedy fresh in our thoughts, we boarded the ferry to return to the mainland, passing the wreck site on the way. Unfortunately the weather had now taken a decided turn for the worse, and we had drizzle all the way back. It was too cold to stay on deck for more than a few minutes at a time, and the low clouds denied us the splendid views we had had on the way over. No dolphins came to welcome us back to the harbour at Ullapool, but there were plenty of skuas and gannets on patrol, diving spectacularly from a height whenever they spied a meal below.

In Ullapool itself, we hurried along the quay in the soft rain to the Ferry Boat Inn, where we had reserved a room. Dripping only slightly, we made our way upstairs to a fine room, with an even finer view of the loch and the harbour. Its restaurant, too, comes highly commended, but we had neglected to book a table at the same time as the room. We were promised dinner at a table in the bar, but advised to arrive well before the 'session' began at eight. The Ferry Boat's other claim to fame is the traditional music sessions it hosts regularly, and the real reason we chose to stay in Ullapool for the night.

In good time, we descended to the bar, and a corner table close to where the action should commence, and ordered our meal. Certainly I would return for such food alone! Smoked salmon and brown bread, followed by slow roast pork belly and a glass of house wine. Perfect! Our fellow bar diners were clearly enjoying their meals too, but probably all had come primarily for 'the session'. Towards the appointed time, the remaining space began to fill with a varied clientele, visitors and locals. An American lady sat next to us. No longer a visitor, she had come from California on a teacher exchange programme and had married on Lewis before recently moving to mainland. I asked if she had studied Gaelic, which she had, getting by with the locals on Lewis. As we tried out a few words, the musicians arrived in dribs and drabs. It soon became clear that most were in fact from England. But Celtic music travels well, and is often at its best when not too pure. They had a good collection of instruments, guitar, mandolin, squeeze box, violin and flutes, to add variety.

Soon after the session got underway, a local man stood up and sang in Gaelic, unaccompanied. It was quite a moving performance. As he resumed his seat, visitors who introduced themselves as Cambridge students from Poland, asked for translation. The singer demurred so I suggested it was about lost love, an unfaithful woman, heartache (based on the few words I understood, and my knowledge that many unaccompanied ballads in Irish are about these subjects). The singer nodded assent, but then thought I had more Gaelic than I did, and engaged me earnestly in conversation, thankfully in English! The session continued enthusiastically with lively jigs and reels played skilfully on the range of instruments. I am always amazed watching musicians play these traditional melodies. To my untrained ear, it seems they build up a pace, and then continue a lively pattern not seeming to head to any conclusion, but, as if on some invisible signal, the fiddlers all draw to a final chord together. The evening continued with many more songs, including a couple more turns from the audience and again from my new friend. Towards the end of a fine evening, he stood up and explained that the next song he would sing was a tribute to Shakin' Stevens, - 'This Old House...'and he invited everyone to join in. While this may seem quite a strange song for a traditional music evening, it was obviously quite natural for a man who loved to sing, Gaelic, English or American, and confirmed my belief that good songs travel well.

As the evening drew to a close we set off to bed, in preparation for an early breakfast to catch the first ferry. We were too early for the full Scottish cooked breakfast, but enjoyed a buffet and good coffee then it was back on the bus to Inverness and more coffee in the Victorian Market. We had a little time for some research in the library and the museum.

Gaelic is available in the Scottish Parliament, and seems to be being pushed as the 'real' language of Scotland. But only 1.9% speaks, reads or understands anything of the language. It would be something of a travesty if 'restoration' became a political issue. Study of any language brings huge intellectual rewards for those who wish to do so, but my experience from Ireland is that 'language restoration' can easily become a darker force. Like Scotland, English is overwhelmingly Ireland's main language. But an ambiguity has grown up, where Irish (we always say Irish, never Gaelic) is spoken of as the real national language; English is viewed as second best.  We fail to treasure English, the language the world uses and the language to which Ireland, and Irish writing, has contributed so much.

In the museum, there are excellent displays covering the whole history of the area.  With my experience of the language, the displays of most interest to me were those covering the transition from Pictish culture to Gaelic.  The Pictish language, which more closely resembled Welsh than Gaelic, was completely replaced when the Irish colonizers arrived.  Other displays gave the opportunity to hear Gaelic spoken, with the words written and translated.  Even with my limited Irish, I found I could easily read the written Gaelic and understand its meaning despite its different spelling.  However the spoken version on the soundtrack was almost unintelligible to me.

We rounded off our Scottish trip with visits to friends, first near Pitlochry, then on Black Isle.  This had us backtracking up and down the railway line through the Spey Valley and across the Pass of Drumochter to Glen Garry.  It all became very familiar, until we finally said goodbye to Inverness and took the early morning train, direct to Kings Cross, and then home.  All in all, we rated the visit a huge success, and spent some hours on the way back plotting the next Scottish visit, and so the next coastal station.

---

[1] www.metoffice.gov.uk/weather/marine/guide/beaufortscale.html

[2] For more information, see the wonderful article from 'A History of the World in 100 Objects' available as downloads from the BBC website.

# Lerwick

60° 7′ N        1° 7′ W

East northeast 7, 25 miles, Fair, 1017, Rising

December 2009

As the northern-most coastal station on my list, the most extreme among extremes as far as I was concerned, I was tempted to try to make my visit at one of the day-length extremes, midsummer or midwinter. The more I considered it, the more I was tempted to try midwinter. At first, Ginny thought I was crazy. She imagined raging storms in the North Sea, hours of seasickness, in short, no fun at all. But I persisted, and rather than be left behind she reluctantly agreed to my plan. Secretly I think she was quite happy to take on the challenge. In truth, travelling to Shetland is not too difficult. From King's Cross there is a direct train to Aberdeen, and from there every night of the year a ferry leaves for Lerwick. What could be simpler?

Perhaps surprisingly I have a number of different connections with Shetland. My first visit there was a holiday when Ginny and I flew to Sumburgh, at the south of the main island in 1990, taking our bikes. I think we imagined relatively easy cycling around the islands that make up the Shetland group. The cycling itself was not difficult but the distances involved and the persistent wind made for long and tiring days.  But we enjoyed the islands immensely; their stark beauty, wild scenery, Viking history, fantastic seabird colonies and friendly people made for a very enjoyable visit.  But I do remember a dark cloud: the main news item of that visit was the Iraqi invasion of Kuwait.

I also had business connections with Shetland.  In 1980 I started work with a small specialist engineering consultancy engaged in project planning for the BP Sullom Voe terminal, then being constructed to receive oil through pipelines from the new oilfields under the North Sea.  Unfortunately I did not have the chance to visit but on our 1990 trip I had the satisfaction of seeing the terminal in full operation, and the knowledge that I had played a (very) small part in a huge enterprise.  Another specialist company, Kildrummy, worked on that terminal and then established its headquarters in Lerwick.  I started working with Kildrummy in 1995, a relationship which continues to the present day.  On their behalf I have travelled to Shetland, and also participated in other oil projects in many countries: India, Malaysia, Australia and the United States for example.

The third connection I have with Shetland concerns my sailing trips in the Pacific.  Like many island communities, Shetland has a long tradition of sending young men to work at sea, in the Navy, on merchant ships and more recently on ships supplying the oil and gas fields offshore.  On my original Pacific voyage aboard *Soren Larsen*, from Panama to Tahiti in 2001, the second officer, Barry, was a Shetlander.  On subsequent trips, he became first officer and then later captain of the ship.  Since finding crew for square-rigged ships is always a problem, frequently news of opportunities involves references from friends.   So *Soren Larsen* has had carpenters, engineers and another captain from Shetland since then.

Being midwinter, when we left Dorking it was still the twilight before the dawn.  The sky was clear and there was frost on the ground as we walked to the station, with mist seeping up the river valley.  But the trains were all running on time, and we reached

King's Cross in good time for our train to Aberdeen. Looking at the departure board I was childishly pleased to see that the train was called 'Northern Lights'; it seemed an appropriate name on which to begin our winter journey. And on the list of destinations where the train would call was Leuchars, an old friend by now. Our other journeys north have tended to be in the summer, with blue skies and busy fields. But looking out the carriage window now as we travelled north, we could see a low grey sky, seemingly resting on the hedgerows. Winter fields, dull winter pastures and muddy winter wheat stretched out from the railway track. Bare trees stood in the hedgerows, home to bedraggled rooks and crows.

On such a long journey, not surprisingly we had many different passengers joining and leaving. At Newcastle a small Chinese group joined the train and sat near us. Opposite us sat a young couple, close together, sharing an iPod and exchanging sweet gentle words and gestures. An older man travelling with them sat on the other side of the aisle. Though they talked together in Mandarin, the older man was reading a book in English, entitled 'On Achieving Buddhahood in this lifetime'. Personally I thought the young couple were well on the way achieving it.

Though it was a long journey, it was punctuated with scenic highlights: Durham, the Angel of the North, crossing the Tyne, Edinburgh and then the journey across the Forth Bridge as the sun was setting. We stopped briefly at Leuchars in the gloom and then continued onwards to the Tay Bridge and Dundee in the dark. Outside, what little we could see was dark hills, but this time no heather, just wet fields and woodland.

Aberdeen in the early evening, with Christmas just 10 days away, was busy and bright. We found our way down to the quay from the station, passing through Union Square, a very new looking shopping centre adjoining the station. I'm not sure how many people walk this route, but despite the busy port traffic, it's easy and pedestrian friendly enough. Turning a corner, we saw our ferry, small but perfect, tied up and ready. Called M.V. Hrossy, it was built in Finland specifically for this route about ten years ago. The population of Shetland is about 25,000, similar to that of Dorking. There is a ferry between Aberdeen and Lerwick every night, in each direction. In addition, there are regular air services between Shetland and the mainland. So it should not have been a surprise that there were not many passengers, in fact, on the voyage, there were more crew than passengers. There were some vehicular passengers, and I suppose some freight. But there is an additional freight ferry service. For a small island community, Shetland is extremely well connected with the outside world. We could only speculate as to who the passengers were. Workers? Returning shoppers? Visitors? At this time of year? Who else would be so crazy!

Our cabin was ideal: bright and clean with full facilities and a large window. The forecast as we left in the morning had been good, but an updated forecast displayed at the purser's desk gave a little cause for concern. It suggested a wind force of 5 to 6 from the North and the sea state moderate to rough for sea areas Cromarty and Fair Isle, the areas we would be travelling through. Since we would be heading north, we would be heading directly into any rough seas. But it was too late to change our minds, so we contented ourselves with a light meal from the canteen, and a couple of anti-seasickness pills.

Slightly ahead of the 7.00 pm scheduled departure time the ferry pulled away from the quay for its twelve-hour crossing to Lerwick. We heard the usual safety announcements in our cabin, then climbed to the deck to watch Aberdeen slip away astern. The inner harbour at Aberdeen contained about half a dozen huge oil rig supply boats, in harbour to load and unload supplies to keep the offshore platforms working smoothly. Beyond the harbour we passed a line of ships at anchor; many of these, as with the harbour itself, were lit up with coloured lights for Christmas. Behind the city, the sky looked very dark, with clouds glowing purple from the city lights low over the hinterland. Passing yet more ships, some leaving, some arriving, we moved steadily out into the inky night, a bubble of light in the moonless dark. Above we could just make out a sprinkling of stars, as the clouds began to thin. Along the

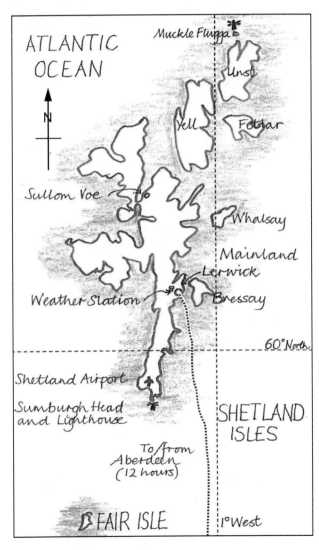

shore, lights and settlements thinned out as we moved away from the city. When we could make out the lighthouse at Rattray Head in the distance, we decided it was time to go below to our cabin to sleep.

In fact the forecast may have been a little pessimistic: we had a quiet night. The ship was pretty stable with just the odd wave reminding us that we were at sea. In the morning the first indication we had of our arrival was the beam from the Sumburgh Head Lighthouse sweeping our cabin window. Back up on deck, it was still dark. A string of lighthouses up the coast guided us towards the lights of Lerwick, and our scheduled arrival around 7.00 am. The purser made an announcement asking passengers to please take their cars ashore as soon as the ship docked, and then return for breakfast should they wish to do so. He emphasised that there was no need to leave cabins before about 9.00 am, very useful for us. All in all, the crossing was not so extreme!

At 9.00 am as we left the ship, it was still dark. I had arranged with my colleagues at Kildrummy to collect the key to our accommodation from them, so their office was our first stop in Lerwick. Ginny had not met many of the Kildrummy team from Lerwick before so she was pleased to do so now, having heard most of their names and having spoken to many of them.

We settled in our lodgings and then set out to explore the town. First stop was a walk back to the port to take pictures of the ship now that the sun had risen. Throughout the morning, the sky brightened but at these latitudes, 60° north, the maximum height of the sun above the horizon at midday during the middle of December is only about 7°. Sunrise is around 9:30 am and sunset around 3:30 pm. Between these times the sun crawls along just above the horizon, producing dramatic effects as it lights the clouds from beneath and casts long shadows all day.

Like the Western Isles, Shetland has virtually no trees. Having left late autumn in the south, with wet leaves blowing everywhere, it was odd to be here, and see no trees at all. Occasionally we would see a leaf and wonder where it came from. At a distance you might imagine it to be a doggie dropping, not expecting to see a leaf!

Walking around the town, we stopped to examine the fort which had been built originally to deter Dutch raiders, during one of the many wars between England and the Netherlands. It seems to have been singularly ineffective since the Dutch landed and burned it anyway. It was then rebuilt during the American War of Independence when John Paul Jones was on the loose in these waters. Remembering what I have learnt of Mr Jones following my visit to Bridlington, I was amused to find him described here as a renegade Scot!

Lerwick has a nice selection of small shops, some of which stock a strange mix of goods: for example trail bikes alongside kids' toys. Not too many of the multiple chain stores have come this far north. We also visited the tourist office, and were not surprised to find it very quiet at this time of year. Lerwick is a small place, and later in the day we bumped into a lady who remembered seeing us in the tourist office and had wondered at who the tourists could be!

Around the town are many reminders of Shetland's links with the sea. There is an Arthur Anderson school, named after a benefactor, a native of Lerwick who went on to be chairman of P&O Shipping, as well as being a Member of Parliament for these islands. The war memorial shows hundreds of deaths in the First and Second World Wars, largely, as you might expect, young men lost at sea, either in the Navy or on merchant ships.

We noticed rubbish bags covered with heavy netting, to keep the seagulls, known in Shetland as 'scories', from spreading the contents over the footpaths. Another feature we noticed in Lerwick was a surprising number of churches. Mostly small, and with a very specific mission, they seem to be on every street corner. Several were dedicated to congregations from overseas, Norway and Russia for instance.

In playing host to the international oil business, Shetland negotiated a deal to retain a small share of the value of the oil passing through the Sullom Voe terminal. This revenue has been used to support community activities, with libraries, swimming pools and leisure centres being built throughout the islands. It also supports education; Shetland has some of the best performing schools in Scotland, despite the small population being distributed across difficult terrain.

While planning my visit to Shetland, I had telephoned the weather station to ask if the visit would be possible. At Leuchars, Alec had told us that Lerwick launched weather balloons, in a similar manner to those at the Valencia, where we were lucky to arrive as the balloon launch was being prepared. When I called Lerwick to ask about a visit, and the launch time, I was told if possible to arrange my visit for Wednesday. Though they launch balloons every day, each Wednesday they launch a larger instrument package, which includes an ozone monitor.

On Wednesday morning as suggested, we walked out from the centre of Lerwick past a new Tesco supermarket, and an ancient Pictish Broch, to the weather station. New housing is developing all around Lerwick, and soon will be encroaching on the weather station near the top of the hill. From the outside the weather station looks very functional, with the usual array of instruments on its roof. Nearby houses were clearly built in the distant past for staff at the weather station, but have probably long ago been sold off.

Arriving at the weather station, we met Martin, the chief to whom I had spoken on the phone. Though busy, he welcomed us and introduced us to Peter and Paul who were preparing the ozone instruments for launch. The package itself was contained in an expanded polystyrene box about the size of a child's lunchbox. This appeared to be sealed together with duct tape and string, a down-to-earth approach to our highflying objective. Peter explained that the instruments are run for 24 hours in advance of launch to ensure correct calibration. This had been completed and the final calibration and radio check, for which the box was hung from a concrete pillar outside the office, was about to start.

Once this was complete Peter and Paul led us outside to the balloon launch shed. We had seen this earlier, on our walk to the weather station and had wondered what it might be. About the size of a double garage, and twice as high, it is constructed so that it can rotate through 360°. This ensures that the launch shed can always be positioned with its back to the wind, so when the doors are opened the balloon can be launched out downwind of the shed. Inside the shed, Paul began filling the balloon while Peter attached the instrument package and a bright orange parachute to the underside of the balloon. When inflated, the balloon was about 2 metres in diameter and the instrument package dangled another 2 metres below it. We stood back and watched as the balloon was led out of the shed and released into a clear gusty sky. The instrument packages, though costly, are not recovered. The attached parachute is simply designed to slow the descent and reduce any impact. Until recently, balloons were filled with hydrogen, which I had seen used in Valencia, but now helium is used to inflate them. We watched the balloon ascend towards the clouds, with its parachute and instrument package dangling below. Then we returned to the building to check the transmissions as the instrument readings were received. As the balloon ascended, I was amazed at just how quickly the air pressure dropped. The balloon would continue its ascent until the pressure dropped to about 2 mbar, 0.2% of the air pressure at ground level. By this time the balloon itself would be a size of the shed from which it had been launched, and would burst. The height would be around 30,000 metres, more than twice the height at which Concorde flew.

Both Peter and Paul had worked at different weather stations, in the UK and abroad. Peter had spent some time on the Falkland Islands. Paul had been aboard the last of the weather ships that were used until the late 1980s to collect weather information well out in the Atlantic. These have now been replaced by automatic buoys, operated by a number of different nations in the Atlantic. I asked if Lerwick was likely to be automated like so many other stations. It was first opened about 90 years ago as a naval wireless station, and seems likely to remain manned for the foreseeable future. My supposition that the station would need to be manned in order to launch balloons was incorrect. Balloons are launched automatically from other unmanned weather stations.

Paul then showed us the Dobson[1] ozone recorder, the original machine that was used, and is still in use, to measure ozone throughout the atmosphere. In contrast to the miniature instruments sent aloft on the balloon, the Dobson recorder is large, heavy and robustly constructed, with a delightful set of plugs, sockets, knobs and switches, redolent of a different age. As with the Campbell-Stokes sunshine recorder, the measurements made with the Dobson recorder provide an invaluable continuous record going back to the early 1950s. I had seen one of these instruments before, at the former British Antarctic Survey Faraday base in Antarctica. It was at this base that the ozone hole over Antarctica was first detected and confirmed. Although satellite instruments registered the sharp drop in ozone above Antarctica, it was thought initially that these were aberrant readings. But when the long-term records from Faraday were examined it became clear that the Earth's atmosphere was losing ozone at an unprecedented rate. The result of these measurements led directly to the Montréal protocol to reduce and then ban the use of CFCs. The British Antarctic Survey no longer operates the Faraday base but has passed it on to the Ukraine, who have renamed it Admiral Vernadsky. The Dobson recorder is still there, making regular observations just as it did in the past. We called at the Admiral Vernadsky base on our visit to Antarctica aboard *Europa* in January 2003 and we were shown the instrument as part of our tour of the base. Despite passing to the Ukraine, the base still had a very British feel to it, with photos of the various over-winter teams and a very British bar.

Normally, the weather station at Lerwick launches an ozone balloon weekly, but if a hole is detected emerging in the ozone layer, balloons are launched more frequently. Before leaving the weather station, we asked about the future of the site. New offices are planned to replace the existing ones, and the site will be sold. As we noticed, Lerwick is expanding and encroaching on the site. To operate successfully, development will be kept well away from the new offices. Leaving the site, we noticed evidence that they receive visits from lots of different groups, including children from local schools. Many thank you letters from children were pinned to the board in the entrance lobby, a reminder to me to send my own thanks.

The weather station is also the site of a Geomagnetic Observatory belonging to the Department of the Environment. This Observatory is unmanned, and sends readings directly to the main Scottish office in Edinburgh. I was interested in what might happen at such an Observatory and checked on my return. Amongst other things it is home to an Ordnance Survey locator, a sort of modern day version of the old trig points that could be found on the hills and mountains throughout the country. Further investigations revealed some very complex mathematics and practical problems connected with mapping and illustrated the purpose served by these locators. The OS locators set out to help answer the question 'Just what is the position of any given point on the earth's surface?' At one level, there is no problem, we have accurate enough maps for everyday use, and these are improved all the time. I had seen at Valencia how the then new transatlantic cable had helped to determine the exact width of the Atlantic Ocean. Different levels of accuracy are needed for different tasks. If you consult a modern UK navigation chart it is likely to include a reference to WGS84, a standard for determining positions using GPS. The Earth is not a true sphere, so WGS 84 is a method of translating theoretical positions onto the surface of the Earth enabling reliable charts to be produced. GPS can potentially be very accurate indeed, but needs known reference points. For this reason a UK reference point was established at the Geomagnetic Observatory in 1989. But the Earth is restless, and tectonic plate movement is widening the Atlantic Ocean, spreading from the mid-Atlantic Ridge as is so clearly visible in the Azores. The effect of this tectonic activity can be understood when you realise that the Lerwick reference point, established so recently, had moved 15 cm by 2001 in relation to similar reference points in the United States.[2] By now, it will have moved about the same distance again.

As usual on these visits I asked for a weather forecast for the next few days, for our journey home. With the wind coming from the North it was no surprise that we might expect some snow, but could expect another good crossing on our return to Aberdeen. When we boarded the ferry, the forecast was warning that snow may spread as far south as Aberdeen. It seemed odd to consider Aberdeen as 'the south'. At the ferry port, Peter was there operating the check-in! He had explained that being a small island, with a small population, many people including himself had more than one job. On board we met Paul who was heading south to spend Christmas with his mum. Again we had a light meal in the canteen, having had the most enormous fish and chip lunch in Lerwick, then climbed up to the dark deck again as we headed south, past the lights, and the lighthouses we had seen on our journey north. Once again we enjoyed a calm voyage, and in the morning ate breakfast on board, before heading back to the Union Square shopping centre and a decent coffee.

On board the London bound train an announcement was made that the snow had travelled further south than expected and some disruption to services was taking place in Yorkshire. It was some way to the south of Aberdeen before we saw the snow, first on the hills then lower down. Soon the track sides were covered, and trees and shrubs, decked out in brilliant snow, looked glorious in early sun. By the time we reached northern England, there was a significant amount of snow on the tracks, but the train continued steadily, throwing up huge and spectacular clouds of snowy mist on either side.

Despite reports of some train cancellations north of Leeds, and some delays around York, we made it back to King's Cross more or less on time and home from there, with little sign of any more snow.

Having set out to find an extreme weather station, it would have been ironic indeed to have been trapped on the way home by snow, for us an extreme weather event. As it was, the journey, though long, had been remarkably easy, good fun and very rewarding. Now there were just three more weather stations visits to go, but my writing was falling behind the visits. The coming year should see the completion of the visits, but how would I find time to complete the writing? Discussing this dilemma, Ginny had a flash of inspiration: why not look for a secluded lighthouse, or cottage and shut myself away for a week or two of concentrated writing? The idea appealed, but finding a suitable location would be another, irresistible, challenge.

---

[1] See en.wikipedia.org/wiki/Dobson_ozone_spectrophotometer

[2] For a fuller discussion see article by *Mark Greaves and Paul Cruddace*, Geomatics World November/December 2001

# Scilly (Automatic)

49° 55N         6° 18W

Northeast by east 4, 14 miles, 1020, Now falling.

## April 2010

Carpe Diem is a motto I have always taken seriously. Of course there are many variants of it, Seize the Day, Time and Tide wait for no Man, and so on, all testament to the importance of doing something now, rather than later, and taking opportunities as they arise. So, when Europe was blanketed in ash from the Icelandic volcano *Eyjafjallajökull* and my plan to visit Cuba was cancelled, along with most of the flights in Western Europe, it never seemed a more appropriate motto. To add to general dislocation, my daughter and grandchildren were stranded near Geneva, and my brother Doug was marooned with us, having reached Gatwick on his way home to Canada from Dublin. We had spent some time there together, tidying up loose ends after the death of our mother in March. I had returned home a few days before Doug, but he stayed on, getting aboard just about the last flight to leave Dublin for London before the airspace of virtually the whole of Western Europe was closed and a total flight ban imposed.

So now I had an unexpected gap in my diary and it looked like I may have to entertain my brother, possibly for an extended period.

Well, the phrase 'Every cloud has a silver lining' also comes to mind, and also seems very appropriate. When I contacted Virgin Atlantic about rescheduling my Havana trip, they could offer nothing in a timescale that was useful to me. Ironically this was the second time my trip to Cuba had been cancelled. My original attempt to fly in January had been grounded when a heavy fall of snow blanketed southern England. Nothing daunted, I quickly looked out my plans to visit Scilly and decided to bring the trip forward! Trying to reschedule his flight, Doug had spent many hours on the phone to his travel agent, daily booking an alternative flight, only to be informed some hours later that this flight too had been cancelled. So when I outlined my own travel suggestions to my ever loving brother, and explained that it would take four or five days he immediately saw that accompanying me was a better option than making depressing phone calls day after day and then having to daily reschedule his arrangements. Luckily his family in Canada agreed.

So instead of phoning airlines, we consulted train and ferry timetables and looked at possible accommodation, in Penzance and on St Mary's, the main island of the Scilly group. Doug called his travel agent again and suggested that he would like to book his flight for the following Sunday, and they were happy to agree. But as you might expect, we had scarcely finished booking our Isles of Scilly trip when the lifting of the flight ban was announced. No matter, we had a new plan and we would stick to it.

As with many of the other coastal stations, I have actually been in the vicinity of the Scilly station before. In 1996 Ginny and I had flown to Newquay from Gatwick and travelled on to Penzance. From there we had taken the boat to St Mary's, intent on camping on the nearby island of Bryher. The inspiration for that trip had been the children's book, *Why the Whales Came*, by Michael Morpurgo[1], which Ginny had several times enjoyed reading to her class at school. That was a wonderful visit, but at that time, my idea to travel to the coastal stations had not yet taken shape. I had another brush with Scilly in 2005 when I joined the Irish sail training ship *Asgard II* in Dublin to sail as far as Portsmouth. There we would represent Ireland in the international Spithead review arranged to celebrate the 200th anniversary of the Battle of Trafalgar. Despite my entreaties, the captain had declined to put in to harbour at St Mary's. The channels and tides around the Scilly Isles are notoriously difficult, so he had wanted to press on to Falmouth before stopping.

As I left Dorking with Doug, there were occasional vapour trails visible in the sky over south east England, as attempts were begun to deal with the huge backlog of flights all over Europe. It would be some time before flights returned to normal. In the meantime we would benefit from the unexpected opportunity to spend a few days together doing something which his family thought slightly eccentric.

With only a single change at Reading, we had a very easy and relaxing train journey to Penzance. Doug is an engineer by profession, so was pleased to have the opportunity to travel on the once famous GWR, known as God's Wonderful Railway to detractors of its famous designer, Isambard Kingdom Brunel. He particularly enjoyed crossing into Cornwall over the Tamar Bridge which bears the inscription 'I. K. Brunel Engineer 1859.' I think Brunel would be very pleased with his legacy: comfortable trains, fast and reliable. But beyond the Tamar the winding railway makes for slower progress. It was evening as we rounded Mounts Bay, and admired St. Michael's Mount standing out in the setting sun.

In Penzance we had booked into the Union Hotel, not quite being aware of its place in the history of England and Cornwall. But the manager, Howie, explained some of it, taking us first to see the Assembly Rooms, whose claim to fame is that from their Minstrels' Gallery news of the victory at Trafalgar, and of Nelson's death, was first announced on English soil. The story goes that *HMS Pickle*, carrying the news, had met some Cornish fishermen off the Lizard and passed the news to them. Before *HMS Pickle* could arrive at

Falmouth to report the news officially, the Penzance fishermen had returned to port and passed the information to the mayor. In turn he summoned the townspeople to the hotel and announced the victory at Trafalgar and the loss of Nelson to the assembled crowd. In recognition of this, the room now contains a series of pictures relating to Nelson at Trafalgar and a very detailed model of *HMS Victory*.

But this is not the Union Hotel's only claim to a place in history. We all know of the defeat of the Spanish Armada, but towns in the far west of Cornwall have been sacked many times by foreign raiders. One such raid took place on 23 July 1595, several years after the defeat of the Armada. On that occasion soldiers under the command of Don Carlos de Amesquita landed in Cornwall to resupply their ships. They raided and then burnt Penzance, and much to the indignation of the locals, conducted a mass before leaving, ahead of any English military response. In burning the town, Don Carlos burned the Union Hotel, and the scorch marks from the fire are still visible in the Nelson Bar and pointed out to visitors, though whether or not these are touched up when the premises are redecorated I cannot say.

Other raiders also called here, and at similarly isolated towns all along the south coast of England and Ireland. Corsairs from the Barbary Coast, modern Algeria, came raiding for slaves for the markets of North Africa and the Middle East. Up to a million people were so taken over the years from the European coasts. In one infamous raid, in the year 1631, almost the whole population of Baltimore in County Cork was snatched on a single night.

The fishing port of Newlyn is just around the corner from Penzance, close enough for an evening stroll. On my previous visit here, which followed soon after a confrontation between Canadian fisheries protection vessels and Spanish trawlers on the Newfoundland Grand Banks, every trawler in Newlyn harbour sported a Canadian flag. As we walked down the pier this evening, we spotted one or two still flying the Maple Leaf. Perhaps memories of the Armada, or the fire at the Union Hotel, live on here.

Newlyn is the site of one of the UK's Tidal Observatories with a tide gauge[2] to keep track, not only of the tides, but also sea level. As such it has collected records going back centuries which are enormously valuable for keeping track of sea level rise caused by climate change. Measuring sea level is not an easy task. There are many influences on the level to which the sea rises at any given time. Of course there are the obvious influences, the sun and the moon causing the tides, but weather conditions also play a not insignificant part. When barometric pressure is low, the water will rise higher, when barometric pressure is high the rise will be less, and fall more. Even this effect is further complicated by wind; onshore winds tend to increase the tidal rise, while offshore winds reduce it. If you think you can compensate for all of these effects, then what about the land itself? We know that over time, land in different parts of the country rises or falls by small amounts. In more active geological zones the amount by which land falls or rises can be very significant. So you can see the need for very careful observation of the level of the sea, and hence the Tidal Observatory.

Back at the Union Hotel, a music session was in progress in the Nelson bar. This can best be described as Celtic fringe, produced by locals largely for their own entertainment, but fun. But on this occasion, they were joined by various people taking refuge from the volcanic ash like us. Amongst them was a couple who were here on honeymoon instead of their intended destination, St Lucia. Some might think they had made a good swap.

At breakfast in the morning, it seemed that most of our fellow diners were also taking the ferry to St Mary's. As we left we asked Howie if he had any tips for our visit. "Yes," he said, "we always say Isles of Scilly, never Scilly Isles!"

We boarded the *Scillonian III* (what happened to the other two?) in bright spring sunshine. Overhead, we could see increasing numbers of reassuring jet trails streaking across the clear blue sky. At home, their absence, and the absence of aircraft noise, had seemed a welcome relief for a short time, but as the days went by the eerie silence and clear skies began to seem like ill omens, portents of bad times. The return of highflying aircraft now suggested a welcome return to normality. Locally the helicopter service to and from St Mary's had not been affected. But there is also a fixed wing air service, called Skybus, running small planes between St Mary's and various airports in Devon and Cornwall. This, like all other air services, had been grounded by the ash cloud.

Being such a lovely morning, we found places on the outside deck of the *Scillonian* and watched as various items of cargo and a steady stream of passengers joined. The forecast was perfect, calm seas and a slight breeze from the north-east. The crossing between Penzance and St Mary's has a reputation for being difficult, and the *Scillonian* is reputed to have a higher proportion of seasick passengers than any other ferry. But with the forecast as it was we could be sure of a very pleasant crossing.

Leaving Penzance, the ferry sailed around Penlee point, before turning south west on a direct course for St Mary's. Doug read passages from the Isles of Scilly tourist guide, 'energising briny air, filled with the cries of sea birds...' He was enjoying the adventure.

On the open deck several passengers, myself included, had come equipped with binoculars. The cliffs and crags of Cornwall play host to a fantastic variety of seabirds, nesting at this time of year. One of the passengers introduced himself as a 'wildlife coach', a member of the local Conservation Society. They try to put a volunteer aboard each ferry to point out the wildlife and birds to passengers and to help identify them to any and all who express an interest. He told us that usually we could expect dolphins and pilot whales to accompany the ship at some time on the crossing but as it happened we were not lucky this time. Later in season, he said, the waters teem with basking sharks.

I knew a little about the Penlee Lifeboat disaster, and asked if he could remind me of the details. He pointed out the cliffs where the

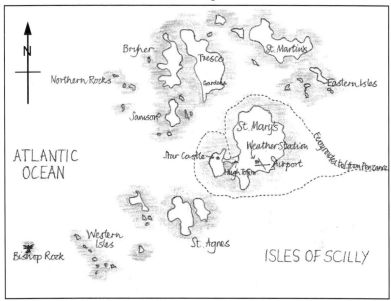

lifeboat had gone down, attempting to rescue eight people from an Irish registered ship, Union Star, in Dec 1981. The Union Star was new, and was being delivered to its owners in Arklow, when it got into difficulties during the storm. The captain was reluctant to accept assistance from a tugboat that was nearby, and tried repeatedly to restart the stalled engine. Apparently he was not willing to take responsibility for salvage fees the tug would have claimed. So the ship ran onto the rocks and the ensuing disaster cost him, his wife and his daughter their lives as well as the eight crew of the Penlee lifeboat which went down with all hands when the Union Star rolled on top of it. Subsequently the rules of salvage were changed so that a captain can no longer refuse assistance if the ship is in danger. On such a beautiful day, it was a stark reminder of how different this crossing would be in heavy weather.

The journey continued, passing the Wolf Rock Lighthouse, which I had identified from a great distance on my trip from the Azores aboard *Europa*, and Land's End, now a major tourist development and marked as 'Theme Park' on the OS map. Before too long the islands themselves came into view, then we passed the Seven Stones lightship which marks the long remembered shipwreck of the Torrey Canyon. Unusually the *Scillonian* took the northern route around St Mary's to Hugh Town, giving us a good view of St Martin's and the Eastern Isles on the way in. We nudged up to a sturdy quay, clearly of military origins, since we could see the garrison accommodation and an impressive fort just to the south of the harbour.

I had left Doug to book our accommodation on the island, which proved surprisingly difficult. It was certainly not a school holiday, and general holidays had not begun. But he had found a comfortable B&B, and we walked through the town to meet the owner, Martyn, who originates from Sheffield. Seeing two Morris Minors parked outside the house, Doug immediately felt at home. Despite coming from Ireland and living most of his life in Canada, Doug is a British car fan. In 1981 he bought a somewhat elderly Jaguar E-type roadster which he has restored (on several occasions.) Since this is not a practical car, particularly during Canadian winters, he also drives a Land Rover Discovery and had recently purchased a Mini to share with his kids. But Doug is also not a person to pass up an opportunity, so when he discovered a 1949 Bentley gathering dust in an apartment building garage close to where he lives, he could not resist tracking down the owner and negotiating the purchase of yet another British car. By comparison the two Morris Minor vans which Martyn used for his carpentry business seemed modest indeed.

Hugh Town, the main settlement on St Mary's, seemed completely devoid of street signs, and in fact the island is similarly devoid of road signs of any kind. There is no speed limit sign, as the speed limit throughout the islands is 60 mph. After we returned from the Isles of Scilly, I found a small article in the Guardian[3] concerning the purchase of speed guns by the local police. In the article the police spokesperson explained that although the speed limit was 60, anyone attempting a speed even approaching that through Hugh Town would likely be stopped. But they confessed that speeding on the island is virtually impossible because of the narrow winding roads.

Having arrived on the island we now had to decide how to get to the airport. Being a small island, it is clearly possible to walk. But Doug had spotted a 1929 Riley driving around the town as we arrived, with a sign attached to it offering tours of the island. We enquired at the tourist office and found the car belonged to Don Williams, a resident of the island for many years and the proud owner of a piece of motoring history. He offered to take us on our tour of the island, along all nine miles of road, telling tales of island life as we went. He asked if there was anywhere in particular we wished to see, so he was happy to take us to the airport as part of his tour. We drove sedately up the airport entrance road, and there was the weather station, behind a low fence, but with all the necessary equipment. We stopped to take pictures, of the weather station for me, of the 1929 Riley for Doug. Personally, sitting in the back, I found the seating just a little cramped, so Don and Doug sharing the front must have been positively squashed.

I went in to the airport building but alas there was no one at the airport information desk to ask. On my previous visit with Ginny, we had flown home from this airport aboard a small plane to Newquay. The plane was so small, with so few passengers that each of us was weighed separately from our baggage. I asked if we would have to pay extra if we were overweight, but the check-in assistant, probably having been asked the same question many times, smiled and assured us it was simply to balance the plane. Whilst at the airport, since I could not request a local weather report, I phoned home and asked Ginny to print one from the Met Office website.

In reality, I could have made a daytrip to St Mary's from Penzance. On arriving at Hugh Town, the *Scillonian* stays at the quayside for about four hours. This is sufficient time for day visitors to continue to the neighbouring island of Tresco with its world-famous gardens. It would have been plenty of time for me to make the visit to the weather station at the airport, take some pictures, and return. But, travelling all this way to such a beautiful group of islands, it would have been a great pity to simply turn round and return home.

There is a lot to see. I always associate the Isles of Scilly with flowers. Long ago the islanders realised that the special climate was favourable to the early production of flowers. With the construction of the railway from Penzance to London, it became a profitable enterprise to grow early flowers, pack them, load them on fast sailing cutters to Penzance and so by rail to London. Exporting flowers is still a good business and on our tour with Don we saw many fields devoted to the enterprise. But tastes change, and I expect the flower business in London now depends more on Holland and Kenya than on production from here.

Above Hugh Town there are large fortifications known as the Star Castle, though this is now a luxury hotel. Surrounding the Star Castle itself are the 18th-century garrison buildings and a beautifully constructed perimeter wall for outer defence. The original castle was built and maintained initially in 1593 during the reign of Queen Elizabeth, to deal with the threat of Spanish raiders and eventually with the threat from France. During the Napoleonic period, massive perimeter defences were added, beautifully executed in local stone. How effective they would have been, you can only speculate, but it's a very pleasant walk around this perimeter, taking in the splendid vistas all around. From here for instance, as from many other places around the islands, the Bishop Rock lighthouse stands out on the horizon. This is the lighthouse used for the BBC 1 continuity sequence where a helicopter approaches the lighthouse in a dramatic sweep. Its beam had been the first indication of our arrival back in UK waters aboard *Europa* on the way to the Greenwich Light Vessel and would have been welcomed by earlier shipping.

With so many dangerous rocks in the vicinity it should be no surprise that the islands were home to wreckers, as well as to attempts to produce reliable navigation aids. The local museum is well worth a visit, as it has much information on the wrecks and on the lighthouses. Doug was much taken by the story told by Dava Sobel, in the book *Longitude*[4] of the loss of the wonderfully named Sir Cloudesley Shovell's ship *Association* and three other ships of his fleet in 1707. The museum has a good deal of information on this disaster, which is credited as the stimulus for the invention of an accurate method of calculating longitude. This is the theme of Dava Sobel's book, an excellent read which follows the development of Harrison's famous chronometer. However the museum has a chart showing the course of Sir Cloudesley Shovell's fleet, and it is clear from this that in fact he had miscalculated the latitude. By comparison with calculating longitude, determining latitude is straightforward and had been known by mariners for centuries. Had Sir Cloudesley calculated the fleet's latitude correctly, his uncertainty over longitude would have been unimportant as his course would have taken the fleet up the English Channel. Still, a detail like that should not spoil a good foil for a very enjoyable story!

Surprisingly there are coins from the wreck on sale in an antique shop in the town, for a remarkably small price. The *Association* was carrying booty from raids on Spanish shipping, and a huge number of coins were lost with the ship. In recent years divers have recovered large numbers of things, but I still find it remarkable that these coins are on sale at all.

We could not leave the Isles of Scilly without a visit to Tresco and its famous gardens. On the early inter-island ferry, we joined our landlord, Martyn, who like islanders I met everywhere, was engaged in multitasking. Not only does he run a carpentry business, and the B&B, but when required he assists the local undertaker with funeral arrangements. So there he was, cleaned and polished, suited and booted for a funeral which was to take place on Tresco.

The gardens on Tresco were built by Augustus Smith, who made his money from trade. They are maintained and developed by his family, and now belong to a trust. When he bought Tresco from the Duchy of Cornwall there was little on the island other than the ruins of an ancient priory. Choosing this site to build his house, Smith recognised that the climate was particularly favourable for a garden. Though often described as tropical, in fact the plants that he encouraged to grow here come largely from areas we would describe as Mediterranean. Smith built tall wind-breaks to channel the worst of the weather over the network of terraces built around the Priory ruins, on the rocky south-facing slope looking towards St Mary's. The warmer drier terraces at the top suit South African and Australian plants, those at the bottom provide the humidity that favours flora from New Zealand and South America.

Near the gardens is a small museum of figureheads from shipwrecks collected here and elsewhere. Amongst the carefully restored figureheads is a gun salvaged in 1970 from the wreck of the *Association*. It appears this bronze cannon gun was manufactured in France and captured by Sir Cloudesley at the siege of Toulon.

The island of Tresco itself is an enjoyable place to walk and to take in some of the different character of this island. But everything about Tresco seems carefully manicured; fields, tracks, the little shops, and the accommodation. It has none of the wildness that you can see on neighbouring Bryher, just across the narrow channel. On my visit to these islands with Ginny in 1993 we had camped on Bryher, and enjoyed the feeling of remoteness and the wildness of the beaches facing the Atlantic. Tresco benefits from being sheltered by Bryher and Samson from the full force of the Atlantic Ocean.

Returning to St Mary's from our visit to Tresco, we took the afternoon boat back to Penzance. Though a little cooler than on the way over, the return voyage was equally enjoyable. Again we had a volunteer 'wildlife coach' to help identify the wildlife we saw, but again we were unlucky, with no sightings of dolphins or pilot whales.

Returning to Penzance, we enjoyed the delightful sunset as the low sun illuminated St Michael's Mount across the bay. Ashore we climbed the hill back to the Union Hotel, for a night's rest before our train journey back to Dorking.

Next morning, we managed a more leisurely breakfast before setting off to the station, along the high street which has the curious name 'Market Jew Street'. Being a Saturday, the train was noticeably busier than on the way down and we were grateful for our seat reservations. As the train became more crowded at each stop, passengers became more fretful. In one incident an elderly husband and wife, sitting at the inside of a table, tried to protect their space while a young couple with children occupied the outer seats. The younger husband went to the buffet and bought teas for himself and his wife. When he placed the tea on the table he spilled one all over the newspapers of the older couple. The older wife jumped up and shouted, "Bloody woman!" at the younger woman who was French. In fact the younger woman had not touched the tea and her husband was very apologetic, and offered tissues and towels for the lady to dry herself. The French lady, not surprisingly, was very upset by the comment of the older woman, but restricted herself to saying, "How rude, to say 'Bloody woman,' how rude." During the whole incident, the husband of the older woman said absolutely nothing, but kept his head firmly buried inside his newspaper. We wondered what his wife would have to say to him later.

Rounding the coast at Dawlish, the railway follows the western side of the estuary of the river Exe. By this time, I had followed up Ginny's idea to book myself a secluded retreat to do my writing. Though I hadn't been able to find a lighthouse to rent, nor even a suitable lighthouse keeper's cottage, I had found an ideal alternative, Peters Tower in Lympstone, just across the Exe estuary. I had previously told Doug of my intentions to retreat from daily life to do the writing, and that I had in fact already chosen a property. As we continued up the estuary, it occurred to me that we should be able to see the property across the estuary in Lympstone. Sure enough, there it was, clearly visible across the water and apparently beckoning me to finish my quest. By this stage, I had just two more visits to make, so I could not put off much longer thinking about how I would crack the hardest nut of all, Sandettie.

Back home, as Doug prepared to finally take his leave aboard his much delayed flight to Canada, we both agreed it had indeed been a Diem well Carped!

---

[1] *Why the Whales Came* by Michael Moropogo, published by Egmont Books.

[2] See www.Tidegauges.com.

[3] *'Isle enforces life in the slow lane'* Steven Morris, Guardian 23rd April 2010.

[4] Dava Sobel, *Longitude*, published by Harper Perennial.

# Tiree (Automatic)

56° 30′ N          6° 52′ W

## North 4, 10 miles, Fair, 1021, Rising

## August  2010

The first station quoted on each of the bulletins, Tiree was to be the second last on my visit list.  It certainly hadn't been my intention to leave it almost to the end, but there it was.  More than six years into my quest, and I still had not visited the first station.  Part of the problem with scheduling a visit to Tiree is the number of interesting things it is possible to do along the way, or when you arrive.  For instance right next door to Tiree is the Isle of Coll, and in fact the boat to Tiree generally stops at Coll.  So how could I schedule a visit to Tiree without also stopping at Coll?  In fact I several times downloaded timetables for the Western Isles ferries over the years.   A really interesting journey could be made travelling via Coll and Tiree to Barra in the Outer Hebrides, and continuing along the chain of islands to Stornoway on the Isle of Lewis.  Although this requires a number of buses and ferries to link together, it still looks like a good journey.  I had considered doing this, but by this point in the quest, I had been to Stornoway, so the longer trip was not necessary for my quest, and so would have to wait, perhaps for a future quest.

Tiree, like Stornoway, had been an RAF base during the war. I don't imagine it was one of Fitzroy's original stations, because there would not have been a telegraph connection to the mainland. Like Ronaldsway on the Isle of Man, its weather recording would have begun with the construction of the RAF base. When I started my quest, Tiree still had a manned weather station, but during the years it took me to complete it, this like other stations, was converted to automatic.

If the rules of my quest had permitted air travel, the visit to Tiree would have been easy, a plane from Gatwick to Glasgow, then a short wait to join the daily flight to Tiree. I could have spent the night there and returned the following day. In fact I had touched down at Tiree airport on a previous visit to the Hebrides. In 1993, Ginny and I had flown to Barra with our bicycles before cycling up through the Western Isles, crossing from Harris to Skye, and then returning home. At that time the Glasgow to Barra service touched down at Tiree before continuing to land on the Cockle Strand at Barra. But that was then, this was a different time and a different quest, with no air miles permitted.

Looking at the ferry timetable while planning a visit to Tiree, it became clear that before and after the visit, I would have to spend a night in Oban. The ferry runs most days of the week but leaves very early in the morning, and returns in the late afternoon. Even travelling by sleeper train to Glasgow, it would not be possible to reach Oban in time for the ferry. And for the return journey, the ferry arrives too late to make the trip back to Glasgow and the sleeper train home. I pondered various options, avoiding any idea that I might again travel long distance by coach. In fact, I had avoided making any commitments to the journey at all. But by January 2010, with just three visits left, completing my quest during the year seemed a real possibility. I had been so sure that I could achieve this that I had even booked my remote hideaway tower for November to complete the writing.

Not for the first time during this quest I needed some push to make things happen. This time the push came from a chance meeting with Andy, my travelling companion to Ronaldsway and Malin Head the previous year. We had not seen each other for a few weeks when we met in Dorking High Street, in the early summer. We talked of this and that before Andy asked if I had completed my coastal station quest, or if I had further trips planned in the near future. If so, did I need a companion? This was good luck indeed, a travelling companion who was not put off from accompanying me again by experiences of previous trips together. I suggested Tiree would be the last chance for a real trip away, but warned of the difficulties of getting there and back in less than a week, and of my wish to include a short stop on Coll. He was at all not dismayed, but liked the idea immediately. The only question was when to schedule the visit? Clearly our wives would need consulting before we could agree dates.

When we did meet again to agree the details, the only possible time we could both manage was the middle of August. While we might expect good weather, there is always the problem of midges in Scotland at that time of year. A further complication is the school holidays, with pressure on accommodation, and weekend trains generally crowded. The former problem we agreed was a risk we had to take, the latter we would deal with by travelling midweek and treating ourselves to first class travel where possible. While MPs are not now allowed to travel first class, in reality if you can book some time in advance, first-class travel can be very reasonably priced. With my Senior Railcard, though Andy is not yet old enough to qualify, the price was surprisingly reasonable.

We completed all the necessary booking in good time, but a day or two before departure, as we discussed final preparations, we still needed to decide on which train to take from Dorking. The 7.15 would give us over half an hour to spare at King's Cross, while the 7.35 would leave us with just a few minutes to join our train to Edinburgh. Being more cautious in these regards, Andy suggested the 7.15.  My own inclination was to take the later train but I was happy to adopt his suggestion.  When the day of departure arrived I made my way to the station in good time and bought a paper.  I stood outside the station smugly aware that I had arrived before Andy, and then looked to check my tickets.  My seat reservations were there, my tickets between Glasgow and Oban were there, my ticket from Edinburgh to Dorking was there, but of my Dorking to Edinburgh ticket there was not a trace.  Realisation dawned as Andy arrived.  Sorting out my wallet for the journey I had dropped the ticket on my desk.  Confessing the absence to Andy, I phoned Ginny who quickly found the missing ticket and agreed to drive to the station with it.  Now it was Andy's turn to look smug, and point out the benefit of aiming for the earlier train.  Ginny turned up with the ticket, too late for the early train but in good time for the reserve.  Arriving at King's Cross in the morning rush-hour, we had just 12 minutes to make our way from the tube to the Edinburgh train.  Andy heaved a huge sigh of relief as we sank into our seats, while I feigned a cool nonchalance.

Calm returned as we settled into the unaccustomed luxury of the first-class accommodation and contemplated breakfast and an unlimited supply of coffee to take us to Edinburgh.  As I had on my journey north with Ginny the previous year, I again enjoyed the late summer countryside unfolding outside the window.  The sun shone on the gathering harvest, fields cut and sometimes already cleared in the south, golden or even green as we continued north.  I had listened to the weather forecast before we set off, also managing to play the Shipping Forecast on my computer.  Warm sunshine had been forecast for the south, but there was a suggestion of showers over Scotland.  Approaching Edinburgh it looked as though we might be unlucky, as we had a few hours to wait before our next train.

Our plan had been to see a few of the sights of Edinburgh before meeting my friend Mary, who had travelled with me aboard *Europa* on my visit to the Greenwich lightship.  I sent her a text asking for suggestions for a wet afternoon visit.  She suggested Mary King's

Close, off the Royal Mile, though she gave no indication of what it might be.  Waverley Station, and in fact the whole of Edinburgh, was a zoo. We had forgotten about the Festival.

From the station we pushed our way through the crowds to the Royal Mile and looked for Mary King's Close. The Royal Mile itself was closed to traffic but packed with performers of various kinds advertising their shows, from the Fringe or even the fringe of the Fringe.  Street artists tried hard to clear and keep a place to perform.  At the top of the Royal Mile, Edinburgh Castle appeared to be shrouded in plastic.  I wondered if this was an artistic installation but as we approached it became clear it was just the seating for the Edinburgh Tattoo.  "Queue here for tattoo," read a notice.  For a moment I wondered whether this might be another fringe performance, perhaps with some huge Polynesian, dressed for the part, demonstrating his ancient art.  But it turned out to be instructions for people with tickets for the Military Tattoo.

Mary King's Close is an attraction using the caves under the Royal Mile to explain some of Edinburgh's long and interesting history. As such it would be an ideal place for a rainy day, but it's also very busy, as is anything in Edinburgh during the festival.  A helpful lady at the admissions desk explained that the only tours available would be in the evening, too late for us.  I asked if she had other suggestions for a rainy afternoon in Edinburgh, and she immediately suggested the Scottish Writers' Museum just round the corner.  "And it's free," she said with the beaming smile.  Clearly we didn't look like first-class passengers.

The museum itself concentrates on Scott, Burns and Robert Louis Stevenson.  It was the latter writer that interested me most.  Two years previously, before joining a sailing trip in Samoa, I had visited his former house, now a museum, and his gravesite on the island.  At the time I had been trying to write stories for my grandchildren, Callum and Abbie, then aged four and two.  I associate that visit to his former house with a series of ideas that gave me the inspiration I needed to complete the stories. So I was very pleased to see some of the artefacts from his early life in Edinburgh, and some photographs of his time in Samoa that I had not previously seen.

Later in the afternoon we met Mary as arranged and found a coffee shop where we could exchange news of mutual friends, mostly people we met on various sailing trips abroad. Mary asked about progress with my coastal stations quest and was delighted to learn this was the second last mission. She asked if I had managed the trip to Sandettie, remembering that we had missed it on the *Europa* voyage. I explained that Sandettie was to be the last of my trips, probably aboard a chartered fishing boat. She immediately suggested that I should invite everyone who had accompanied me on any of my journeys so far to take part in this final outing. "You could make it a celebratory party," she suggested, "and ask for contributions from everyone to take part!" It sounded a very nice idea, but my plan was to complete the whole project very soon so I doubted it would be possible to gather my friends in this way.

We left Mary at Waverley Station and took the train to Glasgow, where we had enough time to look for a Glasgow pub and a drink. We crossed the street outside the station and entered the first pub we came across. The barman wanted to show his skill as he pulled our pints, placing them on the counter, and with a flourish sweeping the overflowing head from each. Alas, with a little too much vigour, for he hit the second glass tipping the beer over a drinker propped at the bar. Not a word was said, but the barman nodded to the drinker, clearly an acknowledgement that a free pint or more would follow. A little later, when I went to the toilet, the same drinker was busy trying to dry his shoes and his trousers under the hand dryer. He apologised saying it must look a little odd, and that he felt like a bloke who had pissed in his pants, though it was only 6 pm.

Scotland is justifiably proud of its railways. Outside the central lowland belt, they cover long distances through wonderful scenery, often with few real centres of population. To keep the railways viable, a number of initiatives aimed at tourists have been developed, along with cost savings. I have travelled several times on the Fort William sleeper, a wonderful institution leaving London at night, waking in the early morning beside Loch Lomond and continuing across the wild expanse of Rannoch Moor to its destination. But it must be many years since the service came close to paying its way. To keep the service running, a sleeper carriage bound for Fort William is now joined to another sleeper train. They separate at Edinburgh. The Fort William sleeper coach then joins a different train for the rest of the journey north to its final stop, Fort William. Other services have been amalgamated in a similar way, and our journey to Oban made use of a similar train share. The Oban and Fort William trains from Glasgow travel together as far as Crianlarach, where they separate, each following their own route to their destination. Both branches of the line have considerable tourist appeal, while the section they share touches on some of Scotland's best-known attractions, Loch Lomond, for instance. So it was not a surprise to find that the train we boarded at Glasgow Queen Street Station was largely reserved for tourists. But I was surprised to see that a considerable number of the reserved seats had not been taken as our train pulled out of the station.

Leaving the sprawl of Glasgow behind, the journey took us along the edge of the Clyde, then up Loch Long to Gare Loch where the Trident nuclear submarine base at Garelochhead was just visible through the trees. Out in the loch itself, huge floating booms defended the base from unwanted visitors, while alongside the railway a fence with CCTV cameras and MOD notices suggested visitors were definitely not welcome. The weather had improved a little as we left Glasgow, but the low cloud which was always there descended further as we reached Loch Lomond, so we could barely see the mountains on the far side. By the time we reached Crianlarich, where the trains split, a fine rain and the low cloud reduced visibility further. With that, and the gathering darkness, we saw little of the remaining scenery as we steadily made our way along the loch to Oban.

When we got off the train it was raining steadily so we found our hotel quickly, and asked for suggestions for a quick late meal, hoping they had a kitchen open. They didn't, so out we ventured into the rain again, and found a recommended Chinese restaurant, a usually safe bet for a quick and tasty meal in most cities of the world. My attempts to order in Mandarin failed to register with the waitress, who was probably from Hong Kong, but she smiled politely as we ordered in English, and the meal exceeded expectations.

In the morning our hosts at the Kimberley Hotel had arranged a prompt but superb breakfast for us, as the boat for Coll and Tiree leaves really early. The rain and gloom of the previous night had completely cleared, and the sunny view over the busy port of Oban was most inviting. At the quay, visible from our breakfast table, ferries destined for the various islands waited, puffing light wisps of diesel fumes into the clear air. Painted red, white and black, they contrast nicely with the Scottish landscape, adding a touch of hard colour to the otherwise soft shades of the heather on the mountains and the grey of the loch. We hurried our breakfast and made our way to join the MV Clansman for our crossing.

I have been very lucky with the various ferries that I have taken during my extended quest. The sea has been kind, and the weather generally good. For the most part I've been able to spend almost the whole voyage on deck, with the exception of course of my overnight voyages to and from Lerwick. This journey was no different. The crossing took us through the Sound of Mull, past Tobermory on the Isle of Mull, famous now as the home of Postman Pat. However it's not easy to catch sight of Tobermory from the ferry, as it's tucked away at the head of its very sheltered bay. Travelling through the sound, the scenery is dramatic, with Mull rising on one side and the remote mainland peninsula of Morvern rising on the other. The earlier blue sky was now enhanced by some dramatic dark clouds, but the rain kept away. The wind increased a little as we left the Sound into the more open waters between Mull and Coll, but not enough to make the voyage unpleasant in the least.

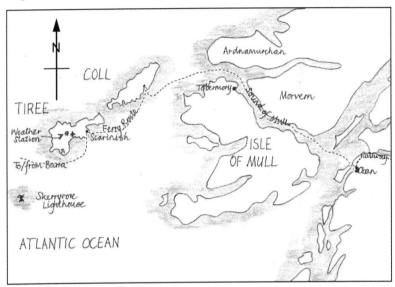

At Coll the ferry lands at a new pier, at the entrance to Gott Bay. In Dr Johnson's day, the landing was in the village and he commented on how difficult that was with the wind coming from the south. But the bay, and the harbour at its head, is far too small for a modern ferry to manoeuvre. I was delighted to see a large group of cyclists waiting to disembark and another group waiting to board. We had planned to use bicycles on Tiree and had considered bringing our own folding bicycles. However that proved too complex and we established that hiring bicycles should be fairly easy on both Tiree and Coll. Judging by the number of cyclists we saw here, cycling must be well promoted on both islands. The main vehicle to disembark at Coll was a large lorry which seemed to carry a DIY house kit; bricks, cement, timber and huge bags of gravel. Clearly if you want to build on Coll you have to put your shopping list together carefully and arrange delivery. No chance to pop out to B&Q for forgotten items.

After a short stop the ferry continued on its way again and soon reached Tiree. Here again there were many cyclists disembarking, and others waiting to embark, cyclists of all ages, including children with their parents. Once a week the ferry to Tiree continues to Barra, and this was the day. I looked with a certain envy at the cyclists joining the ferry, thinking of the journey they would have through the Outer Hebrides.

We went first to the cycle hire shop at the quayside, but much to our horror they had no bicycles available. The assistant was very helpful, and made suggestions for alternatives. She even offered to hire us a car. Apart from this being against the rules, neither of us had thought to bring a driving licence so this was not an option. The other cycle hire shop was located at the Millhouse Hostel, which also serves the windsurfing and kite surfing area at the south-west of Tiree, some 8 miles away. A phone call established that there were bicycles for us provided we could make our own way there. Now Tiree may be a small island but it's too big to travel about on foot. However it has a wonderful institution, a community bus. This works a bit like dial-a-ride; you call up, book the bus to collect you at the required time, and the driver will take you to your requested destination. Not surprisingly, the community bus comes to the pier whenever a ferry is due, so stepping outside we flagged down the driver who was happy to take us to the hostel.

The hostel owner, Judith, is also the island vet and runs the cycle hire. Living on a small island it seems always necessary to multi-task. We were happy to claim our steel steeds, ancient Raleigh machines with functional gears, though the front suspension was seized in place. The advert for Millhouse Hostel mentioned new bicycles for hire, but ours must have seen many wet salty winters.

But now at least we were mobile and could make the journey to the airport with its weather station.

Judith had suggested the Cobbled Pig Cafe, by the airport, as a suitable lunch spot and gave directions. We found the airport road easily enough, and as we turned off towards it, we heard the unmistakable sound of an approaching aircraft. However it seemed rather noisy for a civilian aircraft and as we looked up we saw an RAF fighter aircraft dipping low over the runway and then roaring off into the sky. Clearly the RAF had not completely quit Tiree.

We found lunch at the Cobbled Pig OK, a rather ordinary fish and chips, but welcome since it had been quite a long time since breakfast. Here too we found another example of Island multitasking: the building housing the cafe was also a community centre, internet cafe and the tourist information office, each function well patronised. In the middle of the entrance hall, two wooden sheep, complete with fleeces, stood on rockers, awaiting little people's attention.

I asked the lady at the tourist office about the weather station. She was helpful and confirmed it was still there and, though it is deserted now, how to find it, by taking a left turn before reaching the terminal. We mounted bicycles again and continued to the airport. As the lady had described, the weather station building was slightly to the west of the remarkably new looking terminal building. The little building is indeed deserted, weeds growing up around it and through the path which connects it to the enclosure containing the weather recording instruments. I tried to imagine it in the winter when it had been a manned station. I pictured wind sweeping round the building, rain or mist blowing across the airfield, and the weatherman leaving his warm hut, and perhaps a cup of tea, to walk the 20 or so metres with his clipboard to write down the readings from the instruments in the enclosure. Lights on posts, more appropriate to a supermarket car park, would have lit the pathway, guiding the unfortunate weatherman safely back and forth each hour during the long nights. Not a job I would have relished.

So what to do arriving at such a destination?  We posed for photographs, looked around and the immortal words of Sir Edmund Hilary occurred to me. "We've knocked the bugger off," he is reported to have said when he returned to camp after his never to be forgotten first climb to the summit of Everest. In a small way, so had I.

There was no one in the immediate vicinity to ask about the station, but we decided to explore the terminal building. Inside, on a very small scale and very well appointed, we found the usual accoutrements of modern air travel. From a small office at the end of the building we could hear sounds of a keyboard in use. After a minute or two a lady emerged from the office and asked if she could help. I talked to her about the weather station, but all she could do was confirm that it was indeed automatic. She did think that occasionally the people in the control tower made some use of the equipment, but other than that, the only visitors to the station were occasional technicians. The day's passenger service had come and gone, so she too was about to go. I asked if the RAF visited at all, referring to the fly past we had witnessed earlier. "No," she said, "that's about all we see of them these days." They still operate the huge radar inside the 'golf ball' that sits on top of the nearby hill, visible throughout the island and somewhat dominating the views. In fact, the golf ball was the first glimpse we had of Tiree on the journey over, a sort of ethereal sphere, floating just above the slight mist which shrouded the island itself.

She asked if I had been to Tiree before, and I mentioned the visit when the flight to Barra had landed at Tiree. At that time, the airline was using Shorts 360 aircraft, to increase the capacity from the more usual De Havilland Twin Otters. But the 360 did not perform well on Barra's beach landing strip. Our landing there had been spectacular, passing over the landing ground, circling and then touching down on the Cockle Strand. There was spray everywhere, as the sand is always wet. We taxied carefully to the 'terminal building', and disembarked onto the beach. The terminal was minute, scarcely more than a hut, but fully functional, complete with the necessary fire service. Earlier in the day, on our ferry crossing, I had seen a headline in the Oban Times newspaper which referred to landing at Barra as one of the scariest landings in the world. It certainly wasn't my scariest, but that's another story.

The runway on Tiree is set in a huge open area of 'machair', a type of habitat almost unique to the Western Isles. It is formed when sand, itself formed from broken up seashells, is blown inshore and combines with moss, grass and blown seaweed to form a chalk rich soil. At this time of year it is crowded with wild flowers, spectacularly coloured under a huge sky. As an airbase during the Second World War, hosting aircraft protecting the North Atlantic convoys, it must have been a busy posting. Some buildings that played host to the RAF are still visible, mostly in ruins, but clearly identifiable as military in origin. Now the machair hosts large flocks of geese and lapwing, which pass through on their various migrations, stopping here to enjoy the grazing.

If my intention was only to visit the weather station, we could have left Tiree again on the evening boat, catching it on its return from Barra. But I certainly felt there was too much to see and do, and such a short visit would have been out of keeping. So we stayed for a couple of superb days exploring. We searched for a swimming place, somewhere out of the gentle, but insistent and chilling, wind. The spot we found was far from ideal, in the bay beneath the 'golf ball', but it satisfied the urge to swim. It's a common misconception that the Gulf Stream warms the waters of the western seaboard of our islands, so this should be a good place to swim. Warming, in climatic terms, is a relative thing, and it's true that the Gulf Stream keeps the Atlantic coast clear of ice, way up into Norway and beyond the Arctic Circle. But to do that it's only necessary that the temperature stays above freezing. We swam here, and again on Coll where we found a more sheltered beach, but not for long. Warm it was not!

But the Gulf Stream does warm the water in summer enough to bring some spectacular visitors to these islands, basking sharks. I had seen them briefly on the ferry on the way over, an occasional black fin protruding from the choppy sea. I saw them again when I left Andy at the B&B to explore the wilder north coast of the island on my own. Taking a picture of the waves crashing into the low cliffs, I spotted a large black fin just as I pressed the shutter. I looked again, and there, within 20 metres of the shore, was a school of perhaps a dozen sharks, large and small. Andy had missed a treat, but I persuaded him to visit again in the morning and they were still there. In fact we saw them at several different locations, and again from the ferry on the way back to Coll, when the sea was millpond calm, and each detail of the huge creatures was visible through the clear water.

Both Coll and Tiree are proud of their restaurants, and justly so. We ate well on both islands; local seafood beautifully prepared was our choice each evening. But what do men talk about when dining together in the evening? Andy's wife was sure we talked of our wives, but the truth is less worrying. What do men talk about? Their youth! Jobs they no longer have, children who have grown up and now have children of their own, girls they had met, girls they wish they had met. Unlike many women, they keep secrets secret.

We also talked of travels past and present. Aside from Sandettie, this was to be the last outing of the current series. We had enjoyed the travels together, so what would we do for future amusement? I set a challenge for Andy; come up with a suitable quest! In fact it occurred to me that what we did had much in common with 'Bunburying' as described in Oscar Wilde's 'The Importance of Being Earnest.' The current 'Bunbury' had just about expired, what we needed was a new one, a reasonable-sounding excuse for some harmless fun and interesting travels.

On Coll, the bikes were supplied by Angus, who does the usual island multi-tasking, post office, bike hire and airfield duty, along with some crofting and general maintenance. As we arrived at the Post Office to collect the bikes he was taping a label on each, in case we didn't arrive before he went to lunch. "No one else would take them," he said, "and I didn't want you to miss them!" Clearly no locks were needed, not even one "to deter an honest thief" as we had been told in Ireland. "When you leave," said Angus, "just drop them off by the information office at the pier. I'll find them there, and it'll save you the walk to the pier."

We had two days to explore Coll. It's very much smaller than Tiree, with a much smaller population. There is a tiny airfield, and a service twice a week to Oban, but I expect its main benefit is for emergencies. The north of the island is largely machair, while the south is quite hilly, with good grazing. Angus said there never was much crofting, mainly stock raising. As with the rest of the Hebrides, a tree is a rarity indeed. Having just built a tree-house for my own grandchildren, I was very amused to see a 'Jolly Roger' flying near a small house. Without a tree to build in, the youngsters had a platform on top of the fence, which probably served their imagination as well as the tree-house did for my two.

Boswell and Dr. Johnson visited Coll as part of their Hebridean journey in 1765. Andy brought the book to read on the journey, and we asked Angus about the locations where they had stayed. Boswell mentions three different lodgings, mostly with the local factor, or landlord's agent, but also with the 'quality' as we say in Ireland. It was really quite a journey in those days, not so long after the '45 and the retributions that followed. Boswell frequently makes reference to people using the 'Erse' language, i.e. Gaelic or Irish as they knew it then. I wonder what they would make of the current revival. The ferry on the way out had Gaelic as the first language on signs. This had its humorous side. I'm not too sure how many passengers smiled at 'Toilets' being translated as 'Tighean Beaga', literally 'Little Houses!'

The food at the Coll Hotel really was exceptional. Crab, corn and coconut soup, followed by seared scallops, salad and new potatoes, washed down with a crisp Chilean rosé. The waiter assured us that the scallops were local, so when I saw a diver kitting up the following morning on the quay, I assumed he was the source and congratulated him. Sure enough, he and his buddy collected just enough to keep the local restaurants supplied. But he himself was not local, visiting for the summer from near Christchurch in New Zealand. I was intrigued as to how he had found his way here, when probably most of his compatriots never make it out of London. He explained a connection between Coll and the Canterbury area of New Zealand. A local Coll man had gone out with the gold rush, but found the rewards too slim. However, he had settled to farming, sent home first for a wife and then for his family members to join him. The connection remains strong, with visits in each direction.

Before leaving Coll, early on a Sunday afternoon, we decided to treat ourselves to a proper Sunday lunch at the rather smart Quayside cafe. Having a ferry to catch, we made a reservation as advised. But when we arrived for lunch we were alone in the cafe, though we were assured it was fully booked for later. We sat in the sun outside whilst our order was prepared, and noticed a Scotsman in a kilt walk aimlessly up-and-down. We took our table in the window a little later, and I sat down to an enormous half shoulder of lamb. The kilt man now entered the restaurant, and as it was fully booked, the young waitress offered him a seat on the sofa behind me, where he sat facing Andy. My lunch was as good as I anticipated, and I worked hard at finishing it, though I was defeated by the offer of pudding. When our kilt-wearing friend had left, Andy asked if I knew the appropriate dress for a Scotsman under a kilt. The answer is 'Nothing.' Our friend had sat on the sofa, anxious to make clear to Andy that he was properly dressed, displaying his equipment as best he could for Andy's perusal, and perhaps also for the young waitress. Not an edifying sight, enough to put you off your dinner. How pleased I was to have had my back to him so that I missed the spectacle.

On the ferry back to Oban, we sat in the sun and both dozed as the ship sailed east into a very slight breeze. There wasn't a wave to be seen, and as we got into the wind shadow in the Sound of Mull, the sun became very hot indeed. Being Sunday afternoon, a number of our fellow passengers would be on their way home from holidays, with many young families returning to start school, perhaps as soon as the next day. Children played games, read or ran carefully around the deck. There was much cheerfulness, little thoughtlessness. I began to wonder just who takes their children to the Hebrides on holiday? Given the costs, it can hardly be a cheap alternative to the Med., so it must be people who value the remoteness and uniqueness of these wonderful islands.

Back in Oban we went for a stroll to McCraig's Tower, a strange folly built to give work to local stonemasons during an economic crisis. It has been compared to the Coliseum in Rome, but only by the local tourist board as far as I can tell. The view was superb, clear evening skies and sunshine lighting the busy harbour. It could be compared to a Greek harbour somewhere in the Cyclades, but only by....

Down in the town, we went in search of a light meal (having eaten half a sheep at lunch I was not very hungry) and found a rather too busy pizza restaurant right on the quay. But we found a vacant table and in the last of the evening sun, ordered beer, then pizza and salad and a glass of red. It could be compared to a quayside on a tropical island, but only...

The following morning could scarcely have been more different, dull, misty, wet vegetation, wet roads, but a bright breakfast: a feast of fresh fruit, a lightly fried egg, quality toast, ginger marmalade, but no prospect of burning all these extra calories. At the station we found our train already there, two coaches with largely reserved seats as before, though again many were empty. We left on time, passing out through the dripping vegetation, a low mist pressing in from the surrounding hills.

The highlight of the journey was the joining up of the train with the one from Mallaig at Crianlarich. Our half of the train arrived first. With many of the other passengers, I got out, they for a very damp cigarette on the platform, me to watch the ballet of trains when the other half-train appeared. As it arrived, our guard held out a red flag above the coupling on our train, like a matador, to guide the incoming train to within a metre of our stopped train. After the train staff had connected the two together I rejoined Andy who had not left the train. As part of the joining procedure our train's doors were closed, engendering a mild panic for Andy who wondered what he should do if I had been left behind. Did I have my phone? My ticket? My wallet? But reality quickly dawned and with it calm.

With the low mist we could scarcely see Loch Lomond or its hills above about 500 metres or so. Further on, Faslane naval base at Garelochhead was looking unnaturally quiet in the drizzle. Arriving in Glasgow we had just enough time to buy a coffee then joined the train to Edinburgh, increasingly packed with families as the time for departure approached.

And so back to Edinburgh and the first class carriages to King's Cross. The trains on the East Coast Mainline offer free on-board Wi-Fi, so I was able to check my email but thankfully there was none! August is a quiet time, time to relax, to enjoy the satisfaction of one more coastal station reached, only one left to go. I began to search the web for a possible sea trip to complete my quest.

# Sandettie (Automatic)

51° 7′ N          1° 48′ E

West 4, 12 miles, Fair, 1018, Rising

September 2010

It had been a good year for my coastal station visits. The visits to Scilly and Tiree had both come about by chance and had been prompted by others. So it was up to me to make the one last heave to complete my quest. I needed to find a way to reach Sandettie. Having made two unsuccessful efforts earlier on in my quest, it was clear that Sandettie would be problematic. Following the second effort aboard *Europa*, I determined to leave this station until the very last, a sort of final flourish, hoping that I would not be thwarted at the very end. In reality I had a number of options, depending on how much I was willing to pay, and leaving it to the end increased in my mind the amount that I was willing to pay. Actually, the cost of each of the coastal station visits had been significant, but paid for in a more regular fashion; train fares, meals, ferries and accommodation. The journeys themselves had been rewarding, holidays almost. I've quoted Robert Louis Stevenson elsewhere, but it's worth remembering again, "to travel hopefully is a better thing than to arrive, and the true success is to labour." This would be the last journey of my quest, so I was determined to enjoy it if at all possible.

As I started to do my planning for this the final leg of my quest, I naturally revisited much of the research that I had done originally when I imagined that reaching Sandettie would be easier. In the intervening period I had put aside all research, perhaps feeling that whatever I found out might be superseded by the time I came to do the trip. It didn't seem that that was so long ago, but looking at my original notes it was nearly 6 years since my first attempt, and 3 years since the attempt aboard *Europa*. In the years since I started my quest, many things have changed. Though much of the BBC Shipping Forecast is unchanged, some changes were important to me. For instance I now no longer need to leave my radio set up to record the early-morning Shipping Forecast. Nor do I need to wake up at the right time to hear it, all I need to do now is to log onto the BBC website and there it is. Not just the current Shipping Forecast, but several days previously too, with the previously unavailable bulletin of Report from Coastal Stations.

I checked to see if any ferries now ply the route from Dover to Ostend, but again drew a blank. Looking at the Norfolk Lines website again, I see they still offer the same service that I travelled on from Dover to Dunkirk, still taking cyclists but not foot passengers. Sometimes, I amuse my fellow cyclists in a pub or somewhere with tales of my day out in Dunkirk. Only occasionally does someone guess why Norfolk Lines has its seemingly strange policy of taking cyclists but not pedestrians.

Checking my chart again, I thought the most likely place to find transport to Sandettie would be Margate. A local website indicated that the sea angling boat, *Sea Searcher*, made angling trips every Thursday. The website indicated that the boat had all the necessary equipment and certification for the journey I had in mind. It showed the cost of joining an angling party, or chartering the boat for one's own angling club. I reckoned this cost was the outside cost that I would need to pay to get to Sandettie. Calling the contact number in the evening as suggested, I spoke to the owner and skipper. At first he sounded interested, but a little wary. Rather than explain all the details of my quest, I suggested that my aim was to take pictures of the lightship, and return. Clearly something of my explanation for the journey didn't seem right because the price he quoted me was more than the price of the charter. I offered him the price of the charter, but he said the extra fuel needed to get out into the channel would make this unattractive to him. A little downhearted, I looked at the chart again. Dover, though little further from Sandettie, might be expected to have more options. A search for sea angling contacts in Dover showed at least two, one of which, *Royal Charlotte*[1], went to sea each day. The rates suggested were similar to those quoted by *Sea Searcher*, so I called the contact number and spoke to Mick Coker, the owner and skipper of the boat. Again I spoke of taking pictures of the lightship and returning to port. Mick seemed quite positive, though he checked that I wasn't involved in dropping off or collecting packages from passing ships! As we discussed the outing, he talked of tide tables, tide streams and suitable weather for taking pictures. Altogether, he seemed to buy into the quest. When we discussed dates and prices, his immediate suggestion was that he would take me following his return to port with the day's angling trip, leaving about four in the afternoon, returning about eight in the evening. He would charge me about two thirds of the cost of a day's angling, and the photo opportunity with the setting sun would be at its best. With his enthusiasm, obvious knowledge and the bargain price, I was hooked. We settled on the following Thursday, subject of course to a suitable forecast.

Mick's talk of tides and tide streams prompted me to look at my own tide atlas and to consult the tide times for my proposed visit. I was amazed to see that during spring tides Dover has a 7 metre tide range. This huge range comes about because of the way that tides in the North Sea and the English Channel interact. In school science lessons we are taught of the influence of the moon and sun on the tides, with those heavenly bodies dragging water round the earth like two large bulges. The reality is of course much more complex. You have only to imagine what would happen if the large bulge tried to get past America to see that this simple picture is not sufficient. In reality, the moon and sun cause the water in each of the oceans and seas to stack up and circulate around a point, called an amphodromic point. The further away from an amphodromic point you are, the higher the tide range you encounter. In the North Sea, there are three amphodromic points. The resulting tides can be more easily imagined if you think of someone moving back and forth in a bath, with the water sloshing backwards and forwards. For the North Sea, you might like to think of three people in a bath sloshing water backwards and forwards! The effect this has, with the North Sea narrowing at the Straits of Dover, is to increase the tidal range significantly. This large tidal range gives rise to very strong tidal streams, which in turn shift around the seabed, resulting in the numerous dangerous sandbanks to be found in the area. Most famous of these is the notorious Goodwin Sands. The Sandettie Bank, which gives its name to the lightship and the coastal weather station, is another such sandbank and there are many others.

Thursday came and there I was, on the train again! The connection time at Redhill gave me about 40 minutes to sit in the sun and reflect on my travels to date. I had been here before, with my bike, on my previous attempt. Just days before this final journey, I had sold that bike, still with its Norfolk Lines 'GB' sticker on the carrier. My travels had taken me, largely by train, to the extremes of these islands. This was the final furlong, and I was enjoying every moment of it. In truth, I had enjoyed every minute of the quest, and wondered more than once what I would do to fill the void when the quest was complete. I had even challenged my various travelling companions to come up with a new quest, so far without success.

At Tonbridge station there was only just enough time to cross the bridge, to board the Dover train. Soon we passed through Ashford

International station, now a large and busy transport hub. It was not always like this. Passing through Ashford now, I always look out for the site of the level crossing we found whilst walking here in the 1990s just before the Channel Tunnel opened. We were staying in Ashford, and looking to join the Greensand Way, hoping to walk to Dover. On the outskirts of Ashford, we turned a corner and saw a level crossing on the railway. What immediately caught my attention was the huge signpost beside it which boasted of the large investment being made to upgrade the rail infrastructure for the soon to be opened Channel Tunnel. But the crossing itself looked like something from the 1930s: wooden gates, oil lamps and a little wooden hut for the crossing keeper. I could scarcely believe this museum piece could have survived in operation for so long, yet there seemed no possibility of it being replaced, or closed. I was so excited at my discovery that I wrote to the *Independent* newspaper's transport editor, Christian Woolmar. He investigated then made it the subject of an article[2] in January 1994, which was picked up by Radio 4. I didn't get a by-line on the story, but did get a small cheque for spotting it. The Independent delved a little deeper than I had been able to, and found that this antiquated level crossing was in fact the only crossing between London and Paris. It survived a few years more, but with the coming of the high-speed rail link, it clearly had to go. As we flashed through Ashford, I caught just a fleeting glimpse of the site where the crossing had been. A blink and I would have missed it. There is no level crossing between London and Paris now.

Despite the weather forecast being good, I arrived in Dover in the middle of a thunderstorm! I had little choice but to brave the downpour and walk to the marina where I found the *Royal Charlotte* tied up beside the marina office. Mick welcomed me, aboard and asked again about 'packages'. I reassured him that my intentions were entirely innocent, but told him that I would explain the reasons for the photographs when we were out at sea. By now the thunderstorm had passed and we made our way out to sea in bright sunshine, past cruise ships tied up to the West Pier and ferries loading at the Eastern Docks. High above, on the top of the famous white cliffs, stand the remains of a Roman Lighthouse, within the walls of Dover castle. From below, it's difficult to pick this out, and probably most travellers through the port do not realise that it's there, where it has stood for nearly two thousand years, in use for some 400 years or more.

Just outside the harbour mouth, the effects of the strong spring tides could be seen. Waves churned the muddy water, as it raced around the breakwater, making for an uncomfortable exit to the Channel.    Mick reassured me that the journey would be more comfortable once we got past the harbour entrance, and he would have more time to talk to me once we had left the ferries behind.

Mick comes from Dymchurch and has been a fisherman in the area for many years, first launching his boat daily from the beach at Dymchurch, then buying a boat to fish from Dover.   He and his son now each run an angling boat from Dover. At one time he 'did commercial' and still has a commercial fishing licence but there is much more money in angling. We found the same story on a visit to the Queen Charlotte Islands off British Colombia some years ago. There had been a large commercial halibut fishery there, but like many such fisheries, it collapsed due to overfishing.   Now, by taking sports fishermen out, more boat skippers make more money than they ever did.  Sports fishermen make little impact on the remaining halibut stocks, but pay well for the sport, and help keep the local community going.  Mick agreed that it's a lot less work taking out sea anglers than trying to make a living as a commercial fisherman.   It seems both fish and fishermen benefit from this arrangement.

I wondered where the name *Royal Charlotte* came from, and if there was any connection with Queen Charlotte after whom the Islands are named.  But Mick told me that the name came from a tea clipper which was lost on the Goodwin Sands in the 1800s.  Perhaps that clipper was named after the Queen, but when I returned home and attempted to find information on a clipper *Royal Charlotte*, or the names of ships lost on the Goodwin, I could find no reliable source. Mick was obviously proud of his boat, which was built locally to his specification. She is a very traditional design, with a wheel house at the rear, just big enough for a crew of two, and now crammed with many more instruments than it was designed to take. Even so, Mick had found space for a water boiler, and kept us both supplied with tea throughout the trip. The deck space in front of the wheel house has been cleared and fitted out for sea angling, with waterproof covers for the clients if necessary. Mainly built of wood, she is now getting quite old, and Mick pondered on the possibility of replacing her, though he would make no decision in the near future.

Having cleared the harbour, we set course to northeast to avoid the shipping lanes, and make best use of the tide stream. The East Goodwin Lightship quickly came into view and Mick pointed out how the lie of the lightship gives a quick view of the running tide. He was sad to lose the other lightship, the South Goodwin, which had been replaced some years ago by a modern navigation buoy. While this is clearly visible, and obviously needs much less maintenance, it is not as useful to him and his colleagues as the lightship was, and he is now reluctant to take his boat into the channels through the Sands.

During our journey north east we kept a constant lookout for the lightship with its characteristic flash. But we saw no sign of it until we turned east across the shipping lane. Then at last we saw the flash, every 5 seconds, low on the horizon. We wondered if it too had been replaced, perhaps by a buoy or perhaps by what is called a light float, a sort of plastic imitation of a lightship. Mick had not been in the area for a year or more, so could not be sure of the last time he had seen it. But, as we drew closer and could see first the silhouette then more details, it was clear that this was indeed a traditional lightship, like we had just seen on the Goodwin Sands. I had arrived! Soon I could make out the white lettering spelling out the name, Sandettie, along the side of the red ship. I'm sure Mick wondered what I was so excited about, though by this time I had explained more details of my quest, and promised that he would have a leading role in the last chapter. But excited I was!

I had not been sure of nationality of the Bank, and the lightship. But an email exchange with Trinity House confirmed it is British. When I mentioned this to Mick, he had his own story, that in fact it had been French but Mrs Thatcher had sorted it. The treaty which drew up the international borders in the North Sea stipulates that it should be mid-way between the dry land of each state. He claimed that Mrs Thatcher had insisted that since the Goodwin Bank dries out, it and not the coast of Kent should be the starting point to determine the border. I searched the web for some confirmation, but could find little of note in relation to the international boundary between Britain and France, and nothing about a possible adjustment brought about by Mrs T. I did find some discussion of a cricket match that was regularly played on the sands in the past, confirming that it dries, but little more. My own chart of the area, published in 2001, shows the UK-Netherlands border, but no border is delineated after 2° east, implying that there had been some dispute about it, presumably now resolved. The web search did turn up an intriguing picture, and an article about a French lightship called *Sandettie*. This had been the very last French lightship, decommissioned in 1989, and is now a museum in Dunkirk. Perhaps there is a secret history there to explore after all.

We circled the big red ship slowly several times. She rode at anchor, nose to the steady tidal stream, rising and falling gently on the swell. There is no crew aboard any light ship now, so all the doors are firmly shuttered. Mick had many tales from the past of taking post to the crew, of shopping for small items the keepers might need, and of receiving gifts in exchange. "They gave us loads," he said, "red paint, diesel, coal, anything they had they would give us." He pointed to the red paint on *Royal Charlotte*. "I've painted the boat many times, and still have loads of the red paint left," he said, "You'll see lots of red fishing boats!" After the crews were taken off the lightships, there was a considerable amount of theft, so now there is nothing movable on deck, no lifebelts, no life rafts, nothing.

But the instrumentation that records weather was clearly visible, an array of familiar instruments just below the light. I imagine that the ship is monitored by CCTV, because even though the doors are locked and sealed, there must be lots of valuable equipment around the deck, and lots of passing boats whose crew would be willing to 'borrow' stuff.

Like the Channel Light Vessel and the Greenwich Light Vessel, Sandettie marks the start of a central reservation of a traffic separation zone, this one in the Dover Straits. So we were safe here for a time, out of the shipping lanes, free to take pictures, approach and stand off to get the necessary photos. Mick had been correct about the evening light, and the effect was further enhanced by the dramatic thunderclouds building towards the west. Half the sky was a clear evening blue, the other half a decidedly threatening black.

At the stern of the ship a notice warned of dangerous and unpredictable noise, "Danger," it read, "Intense Sound Signal Operates Without Warning." Whether this is intended to deter boarders, or just a regular warning of a very loud fog signal, I am not sure. But a gentle signal of sorts sounded as we passed under the stern, surely not a fog horn on such a clear night.

By now I had completed all I could wish for; the visit, plenty of pictures, including some of the GPS readouts, and with a knowledgeable companion. We turned for home, west into the setting sun and the gathering breeze. Mick explained that it would be choppy, and wet on deck at first, but once the tide turned it would become smoother and more comfortable. To take the quickest route back, he decided to cross the shipping lane obliquely, which boats are not really allowed to do, but in practice this worked well as there was little traffic just then. I waited till the swell died away to call home, and make my claim, "Done it at last!"

While heading back, the light was fading slowly, and every few minutes I looked astern, checking to see if Sandettie was visible. And there it was each time I looked; at first I could see the ship facing our direction, west, then just the silhouette turned to face north with the changing tide, later only the characteristic flash above the horizon. It remained visible for at least 90 minutes of the journey back to Dover, yet we had only seen it about 20 minutes before reaching it on the way out. Were we looking in the wrong direction, or had there been a sea mist reducing visibility before the thunder cloud passed over? Who knows?

On the way back, Mick had many more stories, of strange weather effects, of loss at sea, of people finding useful or valuable items in their nets and of clients who amused or exasperated him. In the past, the lightships served as a useful refuge if small boat sailors got caught out in unexpected weather. But it didn't always work. He had helped recover the bodies of two people who had tied their boat to the Varne lightship, and then tied themselves into their craft during a storm. But they were drowned by the waves crashing over the boat. The Channel and the North Sea have a well deserved reputation for seasickness, where wind blowing against the tide and the shallow water gives rise to short steep seas that even experienced sailors find difficult to handle.

By the time we arrived outside the harbour, it was getting dark, and we waited, circling cautiously just under the breakwater, for one ferry to arrive, another to leave. At last, the harbourmaster signalled to us and we reached the calm waters of the main harbour. Back on land Mick asked me to help him put the boat away as it was now well after 8 pm. Then he kindly offered to give me a lift to the hotel. I hesitated at first, thinking that my chosen hotel was near the town centre, but it turned out to be on the A2, on the very outskirts of Dover.

At the hotel I settled down to a meal in the aptly named Bleriot's restaurant. I did have the feeling of the job done, quest fulfilled, a mission accomplished. So raising a glass on my own, to myself, was the least I could do. Later describing my overnight stay in Dover to Andy, my friend and companion traveller, he expressed surprise that I didn't just set off after the boat's return to harbour. But he, green campaigner that he is, had forgotten my determination to use only public transport. I could not simply jump in the car and drive home. The train times from Dover and connections at Ashford are such that I would have had to return via London, a long and dismal prospect late at night.

At the hotel, I checked through my digital pictures. Since this was the last of my coastal station visits, I had also brought the camera I had used on the first visit, to the Channel Light Vessel, a Minolta SLR APS film camera, perhaps on its last outing. It had been a faithful companion, and had travelled with me on many adventures. I had resisted going digital for quite a while, but a moment of truth came to me when I was aboard *Europa* in Antarctic waters. I was aloft on the 'fighting tops' platform, looking down at a minke whale which swam alongside, surfacing to breathe and then diving beneath the ship repeatedly. It was an awesome sight, in the true sense of the word. But as I raised my camera to take pictures, I was faced with a dilemma. When to take a picture? As the whale neared the surface there was an explosive exhalation of breath, bubbling up to form the blow, a fishy smell enveloping even the platform high above the deck. Then, as it broke the surface, its huge nostrils dilated, sucking noisily at the air, before shutting like valves as its dive began and its back rolled down, displaying its beautiful fluked tail. Knowing I had limited film, I still took too many shots, but nowhere near enough. I wished then that I had brought a digital camera, to shoot this fantastic sight continuously, later weeding out indifferent shots, keeping only the best. On my return I went digital.

I could claim to have slept the sleep of the just, but more probably it was the effect of my celebratory drinks, mixed with relief. Waking in the morning, I asked reception how to get to the station, how long would it take to walk? At least an hour they suggested and called a taxi for me. But arriving at the station, all that remained to do was to buy a paper, and settle down for a comfortable journey home. And of course start planning to write the remaining chapters of my book.

Somehow though, I could not suppress thoughts of future quests crowding into my mind. Never does one door close but another opens!

---

[1] See www.royalcharlotte.co.uk.

[2] See www.independent.co.uk *Channel train to use crossing lost in time*; 11 Jan 1994.

# Epilogue or Writing the Reports

November 2010

Though I was making good progress with my visits by the end of 2009, I was making much less progress with the writing. My note books were bulging, and I had material aplenty, but getting the time and space to do the writing was proving a problem. Ginny's suggestion, made on the way back from Lerwick, had resulted in my finding Peters Tower in Lympstone, hopefully the perfect reclusive site, somewhere that I would not be distracted by the Internet, nor by kindly neighbours. The Internet is a wonderful source of information, but such a distraction. Everything I wrote, I was tempted to check and look for links. Fun, but not good for getting the work done. Peters Tower[1] checked all the boxes: by the sea, station just a short walk away, compact, no TV, no Internet and it was available and at reasonable price for the time I needed it. Its picture on Google Earth showed it was right beside the water, and its shadow pointed to the tiny harbour at the edge of the village. Close by were pubs and a shop. I made the commitment to myself and booked for the first two weeks in November, inviting Ginny to join me for the middle weekend.

As I ticked off the remaining coastal stations, my note books filled fuller and fuller, and I did manage a few hours of writing and review of the work I had already done. Seeing Peters Tower across the Exe Estuary on the way back from Scilly and Penzance acted as a boost. Suddenly it all seemed much more real, and likely to happen. Instead of worrying that I was not making the necessary progress, I turned my attention to ensuring I had the necessary drafts and information so that I would be able to do the writing. I checked up notes from some of my earliest trips, looked for missing references, and sketched out a story line for most of the chapters.

In September, with the final visit (Sandettie) successfully completed, I could focus on the writing and my stay in the Tower. Though Ginny and I have stayed many times in cottages up and down the country, we have always had the benefit of the car to bundle up our stuff and lots of extras, just in case. But I was relying on carrying all my needs in a rucksack, and if any choices were to be made as to what to leave out, the writing would have to take precedence.

When the day came to depart, I had a minimum of clothes, food and accessories, and a large quantity of notes and notebooks. I printed drafts of all I had done (depressingly little it seemed), packed my laptop and abandoned any idea of printing as I went along. Chargers for phones, mp3 players and the laptop itself seemed to take a huge amount of space. And I packed up a plan! On a spreadsheet, I noted the progress of each chapter, and the number of words each contained. In all, I reckoned I would need to add 30,000 words to my existing 50,000 to have a respectable finished product. Daunting, but not impossible at about 3,000 words a day. To help me on my way, I had been experimenting with voice recognition software. Though I didn't like it at first, my few-fingered typing speed is a real handicap. But, like many others, I do find the physical process of writing rewarding, and even necessary. There is something about the feedback between fingers and brain, with eyes following the emerging text that is very conducive to producing the work. My initial experience with using voice recognition software was not encouraging. The result resembled a speech rather than a written document. But I persevered, and found that by starting a sentence typing some words I could then dictate the remainder, and often another sentence or two as well. Of course, the recognition is not 100% accurate, particularly with names, so I had to read carefully to make sure that as few mistypes as possible slipped through.

Arriving at Lympstone was a delight. Peters Tower stands clearly above the cottages around (themselves built by the Peters family). With bags on my front and back, I approached the door, and entered a tiny but intriguing world apart. A large iron spiral staircase occupies a considerable amount of the available space, with one room per floor, each carefully constructed around the staircase. There is not much space! For one, it's ideal. For two, a bit of a squeeze. There are four levels, ground floor bathroom, then kitchen, living room and bedroom on the top. It's a long way down from the bedroom to the loo, 45 steps to be precise. And the bedroom has bunk beds, squeezed in beside the staircase. Some of the logbook entries expressed surprise, perhaps understandable if you had arrived on honeymoon and had not bothered to read the full description on the website.

I stowed my belongings carefully, trying to avoid too many trips up and down the spiral staircase, then made the first of many trips to the local Londis store to top up my meagre supplies. My plan swung into action. I would work in the living room where there was a desk and stool with a bench seat to spread out on, or to sort my documents. Meals were taken in the kitchen, and I went out at regular intervals to walk along the Exe coastal path. The day was divided up. Waking was no problem. This was a clock tower. The day's chiming began at 7.00 am (again to the surprise of some of the lodgers) and the bell is just above the top bunk. So my delightful sojourn evolved. The words appeared as if by magic on the pages in front of me, conjured up with the help of the ebb and flow of the tide, the calls of the seabirds and the regular breaks, for tea and my walks. Across the estuary I could see the railway to Plymouth and beyond. With the incoming tide, wading birds moved closer to my window, and I was pleased I had made space in my baggage for my binoculars. None of this activity interfered with the progress of the writing; I ticked off the chapters and updated the word count steadily.

Ginny's arrival on Friday afternoon for her weekend visit marked a change to my routine. Her afternoon train was full of children on a school outing, a challenging experience for an ex-teacher. I showed her the delights of the Tower, the village and the walks nearby. Wading birds came as though to be admired, and we dined out at one of the smarter pubs. Following a snippet of conversation I had overheard in one of the other pubs, on the Saturday we set out to explore Exmouth and the surrounding villages. Just behind a huge caravan park, the village churchyard of St Margaret and St Andrew at Littleham was said to contain the grave of Lady Francis Nelson. This poor lady is largely forgotten as the name of Horatio Nelson is almost invariably linked with another Lady. And here indeed, under a yew tree, we found her last resting place, and yet another puzzle. The tombstone records that her son, Josiah Nisbet shares her grave. Who was this son? The answer would have to await my return home, but clearly he was not a child of Horatio's. Did Lady Francis marry again after Nelson's death?

In fact, Francis (Fanny) was a very interesting lady in her own right. She was born in Nevis to a well-off planter family, but was orphaned by the age of eighteen. Soon after she married a local physician, Josiah Nisbet, and the couple moved to England. Their son, also named Josiah, was born in Salisbury where the husband died not many months later. Fanny returned to Nevis as soon as she could to be with her mother's family and it was here she encountered Horatio, then stationed in the West Indies with the Royal Navy. They married on the island of Nevis in 1787and she moved to England following his posting back there later the same year. Later still, her son Josiah joined the Navy and served alongside his step-father for a number of years. He was present when Nelson and Lady Hamilton first met in Naples. Not surprisingly his relationship with his step-father deteriorated thereafter, and he soon left the navy. Amazingly, following the death of Nelson, and presumably after Waterloo, Fanny and her son moved to Paris. Josiah died there in 1830, not quite a year before his mother.

One of my walks from the Tower took me towards Exeter, and past the Royal Marine Commando training base. At the weekend this was quiet, but during the week every time I passed there were young men climbing ropes, running hard and splashing through mud on their way around a formidable looking assault course, while their trainers shouted variously encouragement and obscenities at them. We had a Sunday visit from our friend Lorna who had previously visited the Commando base to be present at the graduation of her friend's son. But she had been unaware of the nearby presence of Peters Tower, and was delighted to make its acquaintance. After Sunday lunch in one of the local hostelries, Lorna left for home, soon followed by Ginny whose train this time was devoid of school children. I was left in solitude again to complete my task in my self-imposed exile.

The second week passed much as the first. Progress continued apace, and by the time I had to pack up on the Friday morning, I had completed just about all I could have expected. The relative isolation had been a real treat for me. The weather had been reasonably kind, with the exception of a stormy night that shook the Tower, and the village had been welcoming. From the station platform I looked back wistfully at the Tower, and the clock struck a suitable knell.

Before finally leaving Devon, I had one more mission to accomplish. The Met Office had relocated to Exeter some years ago and this seemed an ideal time to pay a visit. They publish a variety of notes and documents about their history, but I had yet to find just where Fitzroy had initially established his coastal stations. Perhaps someone at the Met Office could tell me. I took a bus from the city centre, and approached the huge ultra modern offices by way of Fitzroy Road.  Despite a warning sign about it being a 'Prohibited Place within the meaning of the Official Secrets Act', I continued to the building and approached the Reception. Helpfully, the receptionist directed me to the entrance to the National Meteorological Library just by her desk. There, following a quick search of my bags (after all it is a Prohibited Place), I explained my request to the Librarian.  She called the officer who had written a pamphlet of the History of the Met Office[2], and after much delving he found the appropriate volumes of the 'Report of Meteorological Department' for the relevant dates.  Entries were made by 'R.F.' and listed the stations[3] and the signals to be displayed[4].  A subsequent entry addressed by Robert Fitzroy to the Admiralty gave the assurance that the Board of Trade and not the Admiralty would pay for the cost of the telegrams.

I felt now that my quest was complete.  In my bag I had a complete draft of this volume.  Surely it would be a simple matter to check and revise the work, and to add a few diagrams before publication? Or would it?

---

[1] See www.landmarktrust.org.uk and look for Peters Tower.

[2] Met Office Fact Sheet No 8. The Shipping Forecast.

[3] See endnote in Origins of an Odyssey in this book.

[4] See Appendix 1 of this book.

# Appendix 1 - Fitzroy's Coastal Warning Signals

## DAY SIGNALS - (Hoisted for Gales)

| North Cone | South Cone | Drum | Heavy Gale or Storm | |
|------------|------------|------|---------------------|---|

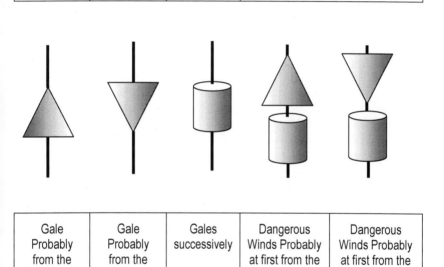

| Gale Probably from the Northward | Gale Probably from the Southward | Gales successively | Dangerous Winds Probably at first from the Northward | Dangerous Winds Probably at first from the Southward |
|------------|------------|------|---------------------|---------------------|

## NIGHT SIGNALS - (instead of the above)

## Lights in triangle, or square

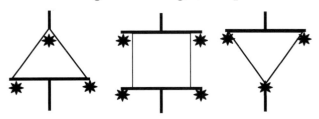

Admiral Fitzroy's instructions for the display of these signals included the following; "Four lanterns and two yards, each four feet long, will be sufficient – as only one signal will be used at night. These signals may be made with any lantern, showing either white, or any colour, but *alike*. Red is most eligible. Lamps are preferable to candles. The halyards should be good rope, and protected from chafing. The lanterns should hang at least three feet apart."

# Acknowledgements

My thanks are due to a significant number of people who contributed to my quest. This includes my family and friends and various acquaintances who encouraged me, laughed at my ideas, offered suggestions, listened to my progress and celebrated as each station was ticked off. Particular thanks to the friends who volunteered to accompany me, or who were tricked into it, Simon, Mary, Paul, Andy, brother Doug and my lady love, Ginny. Thanks also to the staff at the Coastal Stations themselves, for their help, interest and the very welcome cups of tea. Visiting the few remaining manned stations without talking to them would not have been anything like as interesting and rewarding for me and my travelling companions, and I hope we provided a little amusement in return. Thanks, too, are due to the people with whom we stayed, who often provided transport to supplement our trains, buses and bikes, and were invariably friendly and helpful.

The visits themselves were only part of the project as I had always intended to write my own 'Reports.' But perhaps I had underestimated the amount of Ginny's time the editing and proof-reading would require. Add to that the lettering of my diagrams, her company on many of the journeys, not to mention living with my project and my absences over the years, and no amount of thanks would be really adequate. So I will simply record my love and thanks. It would not have been possible without your love and support.